NEW PLAYS 2

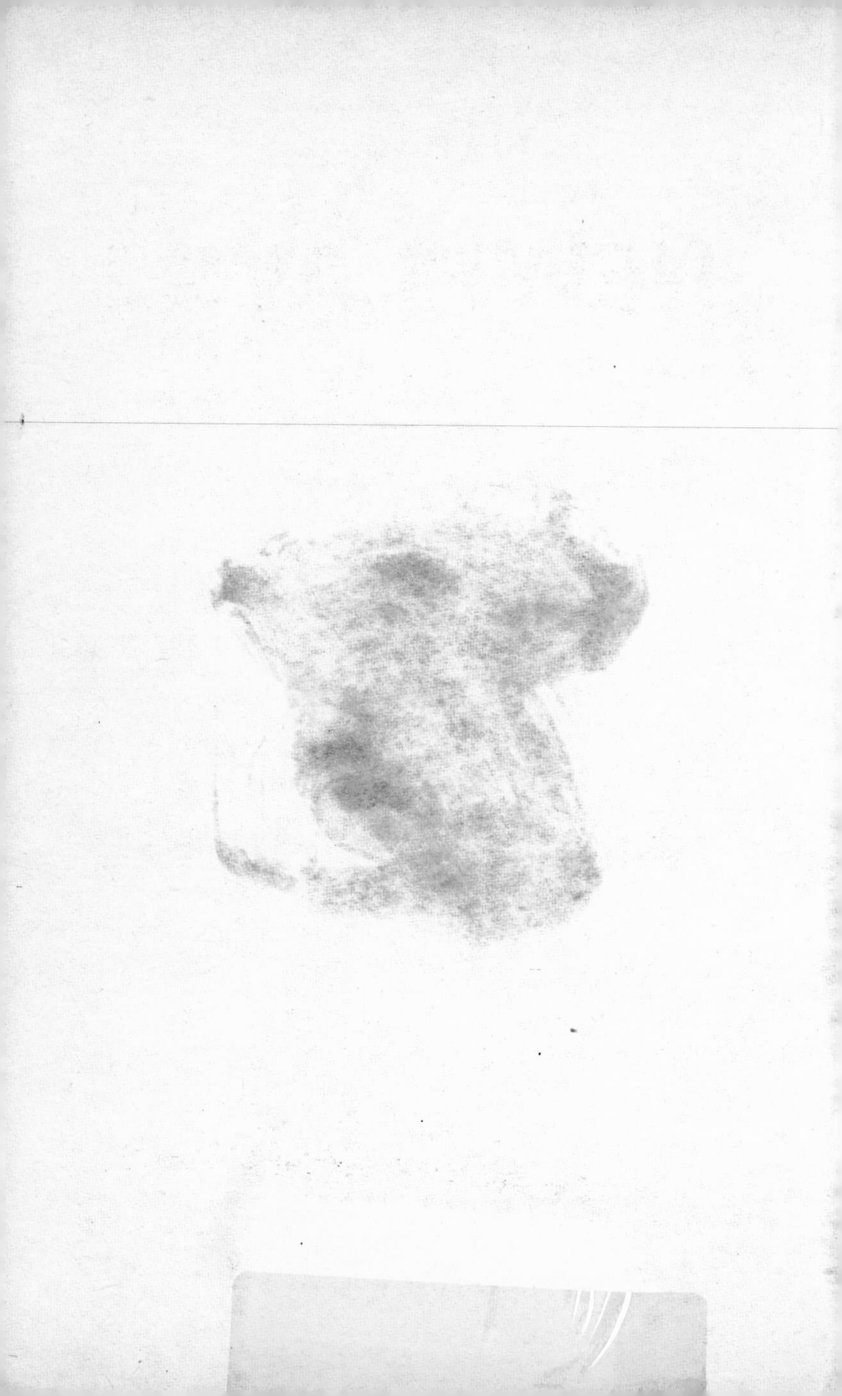

NEW PLAYS 2

GENERAL EDITOR
Peter Terson

Activities section by
Steve Barlow and Steve Skidmore

Oxford University Press

Oxford University Press, Walton Street, Oxford OX2 6DP

Oxford New York Toronto
Delhi Bombay Calcutta Madras Karachi
Petaling Jaya Singapore Hong Kong Tokyo
Nairobi Dar es Salaam Cape Town
Melbourne Auckland

and associated companies in
Berlin Ibadan

Oxford is a trade mark of Oxford University Press

First published 1988
Reprinted 1991

ISBN 019 8312571

Typeset by Pentacor PLC, High Wycombe, Bucks
Printed in Great Britain by
Richard Clay Ltd., Bungay, Suffolk

Acknowledgements

The publishers thank the authors and their agents listed below for permission to publish the plays in this volume.

The Smile © Howard Barker. Application for performance should be made to Judy Daish Associates, 83 Eastbourne Mews, London W2 6LQ.

Battle in Budapest © Ken Whitmore. Application for performance should be made to Harvey Unna and Stephen Durbridge Ltd., 24 Pottery Lane, Holland Park, London W11 4LZ.

Nuts © Peter Terson. Application for performance should be made to Sales and Marketing Services Ltd., Sales and Marketing House, Beacon Street Lichfield, Staffs WS 13 7AA.

Fun City © Barry Hines. Application for performance should be made to Sheila Lemon Ltd., 24 Pottery Lane, London W11 4LZ.

Freedom Log © David Campton. Application for performance should be made to ACTAC Ltd., 16 Cadogan Lane, London SW1.

Waiting for the Party © Mary Cutler.

The M and M Café © Anne Aylor.

Breaking Point © Steve Barlow.

Application for performance of Waiting For the Party, The M and M Café, and Breaking Point shoud be made to Oxford University Press.

Contents

Introduction		*vii*
The Smile	Howard Barker	*1*
Battle in Budapest	Ken Whitmore	*15*
Nuts	Peter Terson	*32*
Waiting for the Party	Mary Cutler	*47*
Fun City	Barry Hines	*61*
Freedom Log	David Campton	*84*
The M and M Café	Anne Aylor	*107*
Breaking Point	Steve Barlow	*128*
Playwrights		*140*
Activities		*144*

Introduction

I asked a renowned playwright if he would contribute to this anthology and he replied 'I was asked to write a play for school kids ten years ago and I've been trying to get an idea ever since. When I've done that one, you're next on the list.'

It sounds a likely excuse doesn't it? Yet I believed him. Ideas are very precious to playwrights and they guard them jealously. They don't willingly fritter them away, because small ideas might grow to big ideas, and once used might be wasted.

Let's face it, writing a play is pretty easy, the inspiration to start is a gift from the Gods.

This volume, I think, is rich in ideas, and I for one am grateful to the playwrights who've contributed.

Peter Terson

THE SMILE

HOWARD BARKER

Characters

THE OLD MAN
THE OLD WOMAN
FIRST SOLDIER
FIRST LOVER
SECOND LOVER
SUITABLE MAN
GIRL
MOTHER
FRIEND
CHEMIST
CUSTOMER
PRIEST
PROFESSOR
MADWOMAN
SECOND SOLDIER
THIRD SOLDIER

I made up a rule for my theatre. When I came to a subject I would ask:

Not whether it should but whether it could.

Not whether it has but whether it might.

In this way I could lead the audience away from the expected into the unexpected. I would provide them with new ways of seeing things. At first they were confused. And being confused, they were also angry. They had been taught always to look for the message. But there are times when it is healthier not to know than to know, when being uncertain is a sign of sense. I wanted the audience to learn how to watch and hear a play without always knowing the answers. In other words, I wanted them to accept imagination, I wanted them to make the meaning. We live in an age of information, and sometimes we think information is the same as truth. We receive news. We receive data. We seem to be told everything, but often we know nothing, because knowledge is not about facts but about experience, and experience is untidy, made up of shame, prejudice, pain, exaggeration, and the correction of these things. The playwright offers experience, but when he offers it routinely, we become suspicious. When he claims it is real life, we rightly doubt him. So I offer no information in *The Smile*, nor do I pretend it is real life. It is simply a possibility, in which behaviour is both good and bad, opinions are unreliable, and memories false. Sometimes characters do wrong things for the right reasons, and the opposite. The same smile means a dozen different things.

[*An* OLD MAN *enters.*]

OLD MAN I was never a nice person. One night the Old Woman killed me. Only when I was dead did I realise how detestable a person I had been. For example, I refused to shout slogans.

OLD WOMAN He never shouted slogans. It was embarrassing.

OLD MAN I only moved my lips.

OLD WOMAN He only moved his lips. Anyone could see he only moved his lips.
OLD MAN And this was when I agreed with the slogans!
OLD WOMAN He agreed with the slogans but he only moved his lips! How could anyone live with such a person? But I did.
OLD MAN This is how detestable I was.
OLD WOMAN This explains the murder.
OLD MAN My awful character.

[*He lies down. A* SOLDIER *enters.*]

FIRST SOLDIER She tried to bury the body. I was coming from the dance hall. [*To* OLD WOMAN] You are having trouble with that body. Do you want a hand?
OLD WOMAN He helped me.
OLD MAN I was awkward. One leg got under the other. But what could I do? I was dead.
OLD WOMAN Difficult as ever.
FIRST SOLDIER I said, he must have asked for it.
OLD WOMAN I said yes.

[*They try to move it.*]

FIRST SOLDIER I said we all expected this. I said her patience was remarkable. I would have killed him years ago.
OLD WOMAN It crossed my mind a million times.
FIRST SOLDIER I never liked him. He never hung up flags.
OLD WOMAN Hung them up? He used them as dusters.
FIRST SOLDIER So that's where they all went.

OLD WOMAN He dragged my husband to a ditch. He was so kind.
FIRST SOLDIER I saw a figure move. Oi, I said!
FIRST LOVER It was me. I was in the bushes with my mate. Look, murderers! I said.
FIRST SOLDIER Oi, I said, shift, will yer? Can't yer see I've got a body?
SECOND LOVER We got up.

[*They rise to their feet.*]

Resentfully.

[*She brushes her skirt.*]

FIRST LOVER Can't find any peace, can yer?
SECOND LOVER Comes of lying by a ditch where murderers are bound to congregate.
OLD WOMAN I know you. You work in the bakery on Saturdays.
SECOND LOVER I said yes! I didn't see you in the dark. You are the old woman who is married to that detestable old man.
OLD MAN Not any longer she is not.
OLD WOMAN The detestable old man is dead.
FIRST LOVER I never liked him. He only pretended to agree with you. For example, when we talked politics he only pretended to agree.
FIRST SOLDIER As for the flags –
OLD WOMAN Don't mention the flags –
SECOND LOVER And he never laughed. I can't bear people who don't laugh.

OLD WOMAN Laugh? I never knew him to. But sometimes he made a noise.
OLD MAN I called that a laugh.
OLD WOMAN A laugh? This is a laugh.

[*She laughs.*]

Isn't it? That's a laugh.
OLD MAN I thought it was a laugh . . .
SECOND LOVER I suppose you want to put him in the ditch?
FIRST SOLDIER If you don't mind.
OLD WOMAN Thank you.
FIRST LOVER Look, he's smiling.
OLD WOMAN Horrible smile.
SECOND LOVER Is it? Is it horrible?
FIRST LOVER A smile that seems to say, 'I've won the day!'
OLD WOMAN Quick, cover him up.
OLD MAN So my detestable corpse was consigned to the ditch, among old cans and pistols from forgotten wars.

[*They bury him.*]

SECOND LOVER Armfuls of turf.
FIRST SOLDIER Handfuls of clay.
FIRST LOVER Fistfuls of dung.
SECOND LOVER I said to my mate, it's time we went home, I feel sick.
FIRST LOVER Because I love her, I took her home.
OLD WOMAN I'm sorry she feels sick . . . ! See you in the bakery . . . !

[*The* LOVERS *go out.*]

OLD WOMAN All at once, I felt like marrying again.
FIRST SOLDIER What, straight away?
OLD WOMAN Yes, straight away. I saw a suitable man.

[*A* SUITABLE MAN *enters.*]

SUITABLE MAN But I am young.
OLD WOMAN I don't hold that against you.
SUITABLE MAN A young wife would be more appropriate.
OLD WOMAN What could a young wife teach you? And I can make myself attractive.
FIRST SOLDIER It's true, she can.
OLD WOMAN I can't give you children, but there are plenty to adopt.
SUITABLE MAN I considered this.
OLD WOMAN Without the Old Man, I felt younger.
FIRST SOLDIER Without the Old Man, she looked younger.

[*He goes out.*]

SUITABLE MAN Surely you are married?
OLD MAN Not any more she's not.
SUITABLE MAN I see.
OLD WOMAN I have a house next to the bus-stop.
SUITABLE MAN I know. An Old Man leans over the gate.
OLD MAN Not any more he doesn't.
SUITABLE MAN I see. I considered this.
OLD WOMAN Don't consider too long.
SUITABLE MAN No, I won't.

[*Pause. Suddenly he extends his hand. She takes it.*]

OLD WOMAN I said, this will be a new life. By the way, do you like dancing? The Old Man never did.
SUITABLE MAN I love to dance.
OLD WOMAN And flags? What do you do with flags?
SUITABLE MAN I hang them out of course.
OLD WOMAN Excellent. And one more thing. The slogans. Do you whisper them, or shout?
SUITABLE MAN I BAWL THEM FROM THE BOTTOM OF MY LUNGS!
OLD WOMAN You are a man I could truly love.

[*They go out hand in hand.*]

OLD MAN I was a burden to her. It's right that I am lying in this ditch.

[*A* GIRL *enters.*]

GIRL I play in the bushes. I look for frogs. Instead of frogs I found an old man's head.
MOTHER [*Distantly*] Come away from that horrible old head!
GIRL It has a smile on it.
MOTHER Do what I tell you!
GIRL I'm keeping the head.
MOTHER DO WHAT I TELL YOU!
GIRL I WANT THE HEAD! I WANT THE HEAD!
MOTHER I slapped her.
GIRL I came back later with a friend.

[*A* FRIEND *enters.*]

FRIEND We tugged and tugged.
OLD MAN Off came the head.
GIRL What a sad smile it has! As if to say, 'I had a rather horrid life . . .'
FRIEND We took it to the chemist. You can buy this stuff to make things last.

[*A* CHEMIST *enters.*]

CHEMIST What an extraordinary smile! It seems to say, as a smile can sometimes, 'I know more than you.' Put it back.
GIRL Put it back?
CHEMIST Where you got it from.
FRIEND Put it back?
CHEMIST In the ditch.
GIRL How do you know it came from the ditch?
CHEMIST Everyone knows it comes from the ditch, because that is where the Old Woman who is no longer old put it.
GIRL So this is the Old Man the Old Woman murdered . . .
CUSTOMER [*Entering*] Let's not call it murder.
CHEMIST No, let's not.
CUSTOMER Murder is a horrid word.
CHEMIST Your prescription.
CUSTOMER Thank you. No, let us find another word. For example, suicide.
CHEMIST Anyone who whispers slogans instead of shouting is in a sense, committing suicide. Such

deception provokes anger in others. It must have been torture to live with such a man.

CUSTOMER And he never danced.

CHEMIST He didn't dance, either. No, let's not call it murder.

CUSTOMER But the smile is odd. It seems to say, 'I don't know anything, but nor do you . . .'

GIRL We never knew the Old Man. But the Old Woman has a baby, hasn't she?

CHEMIST It was a miracle, she is over seventy.

PRIEST [*Entering*] God loves her with a special love. My prescription, please. I think we must agree God forgave her, understanding all she suffered. The Old Man came to my church, but did not pray, can you understand that? His lips moved, but he meant nothing by it. He looked at me with a cold and critical stare. And his lips moved. But clearly, he meant nothing by it. Good day!

[*He goes out.*]

GIRL We took the head to the College of Knowledge.

MOTHER PUT THAT HEAD AWAY!

FRIEND We ran, ignoring our mothers. We met a bald professor.

MOTHER PLAY WITH AN ORDINARY TOY!

PROFESSOR I write the slogans the Old Man would not say. Of course it is difficult to write a slogan. They are not meant to be absolutely truthful. What they are designed to do is to make people agree with one another. I also write pamphlets, which develop the arguments contained in the slogans. And for those of an enquiring mind, I write books which clarify the pamphlets. What have you got there? At night I sometimes write poems. Do show me what it is.

[*They thrust it at him.*]

IT'S A HEAD!

[*He smiles.*]

Marvellous!

[*He looks at it.*]

These poems I hide in trees. What an intriguing smile; it seems to say . . . 'I had a great love once, in a distant country . . .'

GIRL You are so poetic! And you write slogans, too!
FRIEND We found it.
PROFESSOR In a ditch, I suppose.
GIRL Yes! He was murdered. Because he was so horrible.
PROFESSOR What do you want a head for? You are young, you are supposed to dance all the time, go away and dance!
FRIEND I DON'T WANNA DANCE! YOU DANCE!
PROFESSOR I thought young people liked to dance.
FRIEND I want to know about the smile.
PROFESSOR On second thoughts, I think it is the smile of a torturer.
FRIEND Maybe you're a torturer . . .
PROFESSOR I turned away thinking, for every ten who shout, one is silent . . .

[*He goes off.*]

GIRL We took the head to the Madwoman who lives in the cardboard house. I said, can you explain this smile?

MADWOMAN [*Horrified*] HE'S DEAD!

GIRL Didn't you know?

MADWOMAN I didn't know . . . !

GIRL Everyone knows!

MADWOMAN I don't know what everyone knows. I know what nobody knows.

GIRL Apparently, he was driven to suicide by refusing to dance with the priest. [*To* FRIEND] Is that right?

FRIEND Something like that.

GIRL Certainly he wasn't murdered.

MADWOMAN His smile!

FRIEND Oh, yes, but what does it mean?

[*The* MADWOMAN *holds the head.*]

OLD MAN She holds me in her hands . . .

MADWOMAN He kissed me once. When he was relatively young. It took him hours, but he kissed me in the end. First he talked about the weather, then about art, and then about cycling, and then about trees, and then about industry, then about coffee, then about carpets and then about atoms, and I said, All this talk! All this talk! When all we want to do is kiss. And in the end, he did. Is he dead?

GIRL What do you mean, is he dead?

FRIEND His head is in your –

MADWOMAN Yes, but is he dead? Shut the door when you go out.

GIRL What door? There isn't a door.

[*The* MADWOMAN *goes.*]

GIRL We sat down. We were tired.
FRIEND We shook the head to make it speak.
OLD MAN That hurts!
MOTHER TEA-TIME!
FRIEND Speak!
MOTHER TEA-TIME!
GIRL We ran off. We met two soldiers on a bench.

[*Two* SOLDIERS *enter.*]

SECOND SOLDIER We hide in the army.
GIRL Hide in the army? Hide from the army, you mean, don't you?
THIRD SOLDIER We hide in the army.
SECOND SOLDIER From kindness, we hide.
FRIEND Does kindness frighten you? I'm frightened of dancing.
SECOND SOLDIER Kindness is harder. He knows.

[*He points to the head.*]

His smile says, 'Kindness is hard, very hard . . .' Who killed him?
GIRL Nobody killed him. His wife had a baby at the chemist's and he died of shouting, is that right?
FRIEND Something like that.
SECOND SOLDIER I know him. He was my dad.
FRIEND Obviously! The same shaped head!
OLD MAN My son, by the Madwoman, obviously . . .
SECOND SOLDIER I did not love him.
GIRL No, he was detestable!

THIRD SOLDIER When we marched through the town, he did not cheer. When we went to the war, he did not throw roses. And his garden was full of roses . . .

MOTHER TEA-TIME AND I WON'T TELL YOU AGAIN!

GIRL [*Jumping up*] If you like, you can have the Old Man's head. I've got to go in for tea.

[*Pause.*]

Don't you want it?

[*Pause.*]

He doesn't want the Old Man's head.

FRIEND [*To SECOND SOLDIER*] I know that smile. It's the same smile. WHAT'S IT MEAN?

OLD MAN Tell her.

SECOND SOLDIER Shuddup.

OLD MAN Tell her!

SECOND SOLDIER SHUDDUP, I NEVER LIKED YOU!

[*Sounds of a carnival approaching.*]

OLD WOMAN [*Entering*] It's the carnival!

SUITABLE MAN Dance, everyone!

[*The sounds increase in volume.*]

PRIEST Rejoice! Everybody on your feet!

FRIEND No – I want –

CHEMIST EVERYONE TOGETHER NOW!

PROFESSOR You – put – your – left leg – out – you –
FRIEND SHUDDUP!
CUSTOMER ALL TOGETHER NOW!
FRIEND [*To* SECOND SOLDIER] Don't go away, I want –

[*Racket of the band.*]

Tell me what the smile means, you!

[*She seizes the* SECOND SOLDIER, *but he is arm in arm with the rest. They all do a routine and they chant.*]

PROFESSOR [*To the* FRIEND] Can't hear you!
FRIEND STOP!
PROFESSOR Can't – hear – you!

[*The* OLD MAN *gets off the floor. His mouth is moving. The sound of guns booming.*]

BATTLE IN BUDAPEST

KEN WHITMORE

For Kathleen Underhill

Characters

JOSZEF	aged 18
LASZLO	aged 11 or 13
BORBALA	aged 17

The play is set in a top-floor room in a house in Budapest in October 1956.

Battle in Budapest is based on a true incident during the Hungarian uprising of 1956 – thirteen days in October when the people of that country spontaneously took up arms against the crushing Soviet occupation of their land. Hungarians of every class, young and old, joined in the battle. But they had no support from the West or elsewhere and no weapons to match the 2,500 tanks and 150,000 men of the Red Army and finally their bid for freedom was smashed. Young boys and girls frequently placed themselves in danger out of loyalty to their country and their families were understandably horrified at the risks these children ran. Similar fights for freedom are still going on throughout the world; similar boys and girls are still putting themselves in the firing line, and in all probability similar sisters to Borbala are still trying to drag them home to safety. Who is right?

A top-floor room in Budapest. It is mid-morning on a cold day in October 1956. There is a window with a view over the roof-tops to the distant Danube. The room looks as if it had been hit by a bomb. Most of the panes are broken. Laths gape through a hole in the ceiling. The one door, leading to the stairs, is almost off its hinges. Against the wall stand two tea-chests and a wooden beer barrel. The barrel holds five or six rifles and two sten guns. There is an old couch spread with old woollen blankets. There are a few wobbly chairs and a table is in use as a desk. Lined up on it are six hand grenades and six Molotov cocktails (or petrol bombs in bottles).

JOSZEF *is kneeling on the floor, assembling a rifle from various spare parts that lie on a blanket. He wears the crumpled and dusty dark suit of an engineering student with a black woollen scarf at the neck and a black woollen hat on his head. His left foot is swathed in a thickly-bloodstained bandage. His walking-stick lies nearby.*

Heavy gunfire is heard in the distance – a sound that punctuates the play.

The sound of somebody running up the stairs is heard and the door flies open. LASZLO, *a small boy rushes in clutching a violin case. A pair of roller-skates hang round his neck. He wears an ancient filthy mackintosh of somewhat military cut that was made for somebody twice his size and reaches almost to his ankles. It hangs open except at the top where it is held by a big safety-pin. He wears a baggy peak cap on the back of his head with the peak at a rakish angle – about the same angle as the cigarette stuck in the corner of his mouth. He hasn't had a wash for four nights.*

LASZLO God – Comrade Joszef – it's really amazing out there! [*He slams the door*] I counted seven Russian tanks blazing in the streets.

JOSZEF Wait.

LASZLO And you'll never believe what I've just done. I ran slap into a Russian foot patrol on my roller-skates and I –

JOSZEF Wait! Where do you think you are?

LASZLO [*Removing his cap and his cigarette*] Sorry, comrade, but listen, I'd just turned into Passinommy Street –

JOSZEF I said wait! [*He gets up with the help of his stick and sits at the table as behind a desk*] Those stairs are going to collapse if you come crashing up like that. And get rid of that cigarette. Now go out again and come in properly.

LASZLO Holy Mother.

JOSZEF What did you say?

LASZLO Nothing, comrade. Sorry, comrade.

He goes out and soon we hear his knock on the door.

JOSZEF Alright, come in.

LASZLO [*Enters and draws himself up to attention*] Comrade Laszlo Liptak reporting for duty, comrade. I just ran slap into a Russian foot patrol and I –

JOSZEF Who said you could speak?

LASZLO Sorry, comrade.

JOSZEF And try to stand with some dignity. Can you stand with dignity with skates round your neck and a violin case in your hand? [LASZLO *puts the offending objects on the table, then resumes attention*] How old are you, comrade?

LASZLO Thirteen.

JOSZEF Are you sure? You act more like a twelve-year-old.

LASZLO I can bring you my birth certificate.

JOSZEF You say you saw seven tanks on fire?

LASZLO Yes, comrade, and I –

JOSZEF Quiet! And how many tanks that aren't on fire? A thousand? Are any of them coming this way?

LASZLO They're coming all ways – like trams at the rush hour. But we can stop them, comrade. That's what I wanted to ask you. Just give me half a dozen hand grenades or a Molotov cocktail and I can –

JOSZEF Yes yes, I know. Blow yourself to bits. Get it into your head. You're only of value to me – you're only of value to Hungary – as an errand boy. Did you get to Ranki Street safely?

LASZLO Yes, comrade. But on my way there –

JOSZEF Laszlo! God Almighty.

LASZLO Please, comrade. You must hear me out. I'd just turned into Passinommy Street at about a hundred miles an hour and I saw three Russian soldiers right in my path – an officer with his pistol drawn and two men with rifles. Well, they had their back to me but as soon as they heard my skates on the stones they all swung round and pointed their guns at me. And then God, suddenly there was crack from high up in the air and one of the soldiers dropped his rifle and put his hands to his face, like this, and just toppled over backwards. One of our snipers. Sweet Jesus, I'd love to pop somebody off from a high window like that, wouldn't you, comrade? The other two dived for cover and the officer dropped his pistol on the pavement. Well, I still couldn't stop myself – I was going so fast –and without thinking I just stooped down like this on my way past and scooped the pistol up and went skating on down the road. [*He opens the violin case and hands a pistol to* JOSZEF.] Look, isn't it beautiful?

JOSZEF It's not the word I'd use. Did you get to Ranki Street safely? [*During* LASZLO*'s next speech, he examines the pistol minutely.*]

LASZLO That's not all. Now you're not going to believe this. Just as I turned the corner into Balint Balassi Boulevard I bumped right into another patrol – straight into the arms of a big strapping sergeant. He hugged me to his chest like a goalkeeper catching a ball and the violin case shot out of my hands and landed on the pavement. It landed right at the feet of a young captain. Everybody turned and looked down at it. And you know what? The clasps had come undone. The case was about half an inch open. I could see the pistol gleaming inside. I could see it! And this young captain bent down and picked the case up and brushed the dust off with his hand. Then he fastened the clasps without looking inside and handed it back to me. Honestly! It's true! 'Where are you going' he said, 'In such a hurry?' 'To my violin lesson,' I said. 'Where do you think?' 'Well, slow down,' he said. 'Some of my men have got very nervous trigger fingers.' And he patted me on the head and told me to get going or I'd never be another Panagini. Who's Panagini?

JOSZEF Paganini. A violinist.

LASZLO That's what I thought.

JOSZEF A dead violinist. Like you should have been.

LASZLO No, I'm lucky that way. Always have been.

JOSZEF What if this charmingly musical captain had asked you to play him a tune?

LASZLO I'd have whipped the pistol out and shot him.

JOSZEF What, this pistol? Like this, you mean? [*He holds the pistol close to* LASZLO*'s face*]

LASZLO Careful, it's loaded.

JOSZEF Stand still and say your prayers, my hero. Have you done that? Good. Now I slowly squeeze the trigger. [*He does this and the pistol gives a click*] You see? The firing-pin broke off when it bounced on the pavement. A lesson for you. Never put to sea in a second-hand canoe. Did I frighten you?

LASZLO I'm not frightened of anything.

JOSZEF You think you're immortal. A lot of my friends thought the same a few days ago and now it's too late to tell them otherwise. If your friend the musical captain hadn't been a fool you'd be stretched out in the gutter now in Balint Balassi Boulevard. What an idiot he must have been. Who ever heard of a boy in a hurry to go to a violin lesson? [*Pause*] Did you get to Ranki Street? I'm bleeding to death.

LASZLO Yes, but first I had a little skate round Parliament Square.

JOSZEF What?

LASZLO I had a brilliant idea. There were about fifty big tanks lined up in front of the Parliament building. The soldiers were sitting in the turrets, eating their breakfasts, smoking, whistling at the girls. I skated round them slowly. Nobody stopped me. One of them even threw me an apple. Here, you can have it. [*He takes an apple from the violin case and hands it to Joszef, who sets it down carefully at the end of the line of grenades*] I wasn't just fooling about. I was weighing everything up and timing how long it would take. Those tanks have a petrol cap on the right-hand side. They're even marked in big white letters – petrol. It's crazy. Well, if you gave me six Molotov cocktails and I carried them in my violin case –

JOSZEF The answer is no.

LASZLO Why not? I could knock out six tanks and still get away before they knew what had hit them!

JOSZEF Did you get to Ranki Street?

LASZLO Holy Mother!

JOSZEF You should be at home, Laszlo. You should be studying your school-books and chopping sticks for your mother.

LASZLO I haven't got a mother. I'm an orphan.

JOSZEF Really?

LASZLO I've got no relations at all.

JOSZEF I didn't know that.

LASZLO So if I get hurt it doesn't matter, does it? Couldn't you spare just one little Molotov cocktail?

JOSZEF Let me remind you. An hour ago I sent you to our medical station in Ranki Street to deliver urgent messages and to bring back pain-killers and a clean dressing for my foot. While you've been bragging of your great deeds and heroic plans I've been slowly bleeding to death and getting gangrene. Well? Did you get to Ranki Street?

LASZLO Yes, comrade.

JOSZEF Did you bring the dressing?

LASZLO No, comrade.

JOSZEF No? Why not?

LASZLO They've blown Ranki Street to bits.

JOSZEF What?

LASZLO They had two tanks at each end, just pouring shells into it.

JOSZEF The house with our medical station? Number 97?

LASZLO On fire, comrade. Black smoke pouring out of the windows. Flames shooting out of the roof.

People running down the steps – jumping out of windows.

JOSZEF What happened to them?

LASZLO Machine guns.

JOSZEF I see. [*Pause*] Think carefully. Did a man with white hair come out? Very tall and thin, wearing glasses?

LASZLO Yes, there was a man like that.

JOSZEF What happened to him?

LASZLO Shot. As he came down the steps.

JOSZEF Really? Shot on the steps. [*Pause*] A girl? A red-haired girl in a dark blue padded jacket? About 19? A black fur hat? Did you see her?

LASZLO She had a sten gun.

JOSZEF What?

LASZLO A sten gun. She came rolling out of a window and jumped up and started firing.

JOSZEF Yes?

LASZLO It was no good.

JOSZEF No?

LASZLO She lasted about thirty seconds.

JOSZEF I see. [*He stares into the distance for some moments. Then he picks up a pen and starts writing on the margin of a newspaper.*]

LASZLO So if we want revenge, comrade, just give me half a dozen Molotov –

JOSZEF Shut up. Do something simple and useful for a change. [*He finishes his writing*] Here are four addresses. Go to the first three and tell them the medical station's finished and the doctor's dead. They must make other arrangements for their wounded. The fourth address is over the Elizabeth Bridge in Buda. A woman of about fifty will come to the door, a fat woman with a walking-stick. Tell her I sent you and ask her to go inside and sit down. Then tell her what you saw in Ranki Street. [*He has *torn the strip from the newspaper and now hands it to* LASZLO, *who rolls it into a small tube and puts it in his mouth*] If she has any first-aid dressings bring them back here. Don't tell her about my foot or I'll break your neck. Tell her I'm well. Right, off you go. [LASZLO *hesitates*] What are you waiting for? Not frightened, are you?

LASZLO I'm not frightened of anything in the world. I was just thinking – just one little Molotov –

JOSZEF Get out of here! Go on, get out! [LASZLO *goes to the door and opens it*] Wait. Tell her I love her.

[LASZLO *leaves.* JOSEPH *holds his head in his hands and his shoulders shake. In a moment the door opens and* LASZLO *is back.* JOSEPH *looks up sternly.*]

LASZLO Oh, God! Quick! You've got to hide me!

JOSZEF What? Who from?

LASZLO Coming up the stairs! Quick! I don't think I was seen!

JOSZEF Who is it, the Russians?

LASZLO My sister!

JOSZEF Your sister?

LASZLO Coming up the stairs! You've got to hide me!

[*With* JOSEPH'S *help he removes the guns from the beer barrel and climbs inside*]

She'll kill me. Don't give me away, comrade. She'll murder me.

JOSZEF Why, what have you done to her?

LASZLO Nothing, she's just a maniac. [*He disappears,*

then his head bobs up] Cross your heart you won't give me away.

[JOSZEF *throws a blanket on top of him. Then he places a tea-chest on top of the barrel. The violin case is on the floor beside the barrel. He covers it with a blanket, hobbles to the table, sits and starts dismantling the pistol. He doesn't look up when the door opens and a girl of 17 enters. This is* BORBALA. *She gazes around suspiciously.*]

BORBALA Excuse me.
JOSZEF [*Looking up with surprise*] Yes?
BORBALA Have you seen a boy?
JOSZEF A boy?
BORBALA A boy of eleven. He's my brother.
JOSZEF Eleven? I don't know any boy of eleven.
BORBALA His mother's going crazy with worry.
JOSZEF His mother?
BORBALA Yes, he hasn't been home for four nights. He's killing her. [*She steps further into the room, her eyes everywhere*] I've been searching for him for three days and nights – just dashing home for a quick meal. My feet are bleeding from tramping the streets. My fingers are scorched from turning over corpses in the road.
JOSZEF Scorched?
BORBALA The bodies are covered in lime. Some of them are only Laszlo's size. You have to scrape it off their faces to see who they are. Every time one of those little dead faces wasn't Laszlo I wanted to laugh and cheer. But their sisters must be looking for them, too. Their mothers must be going mad. Then just ten minutes ago I saw a boy in the distance going along

Andrassy Avenue very fast, as if he was on skates. Laszlo stole our janitor's grandson's skates four nights ago, so I was almost sure it was him. He turned into this street and it's a cul-de-sac so he can't have come out again. And this is the only house with any sign of life. All the rest are in ruins.

JOSZEF Yes, the Red Army paid us a little social call two nights ago. This is the only place they left standing, if you can call it standing.

BORBALA You people use little children, don't you? To do your dirty work. Is that what Laszlo's been doing? Running up and down Budapest smuggling arms under the noses of the Russians?

JOSZEF I don't know any boy of eleven.

BORBALA But you do use young boys. Some of them are lying out there in the streets, covered in lime. It must make you very proud to send little boys to their deaths.

JOSZEF Shall I tell you something? We can't stop the little devils. We tell them to go home and chop wood for their mothers but somehow the instinct to fight for freedom seems to have nothing to do with age. They're born with it.

BORBALA Fighting for freedom? My God, if only those boys knew it, you so-called freedom fighters are worse than the Russians. The Russians are only taking their country. You're taking their lives. You're taking everything.

JOSZEF Except their soul.

BORBALA [*Laughing derisively*] Their soul? What's that?

JOSZEF I've no idea. Yes, I have. It's something inside – something that makes us take life seriously.

BORBALA And you think it's serious to throw life away?

JOSZEF It's the most serious thing of all.

BORBALA It isn't serious, it's crazy! Listen, brother, I want to live, live, live. Every morning and every night I throw myself down on my knees and thank God for the gift of life. Before I die I want to do one thing brilliantly well – otherwise I'm not going to die. I've got a thousand plans, a thousand possibilities, a thousand future friends I haven't even met, and without life – life – they're not worth that! [*She snaps her fingers*]

JOSZEF God, how I agree with you. Life's a gift – a glorious gift. But one to be used, not an ornament to put on a high shelf in case it gets cracked. It comes wrapped in many layers of paper, this gift, and to peel off the layers is to go on asking questions, to keep seeking the truth. Each new layer is a new discovery –science – music – art – anything you like – and with each new layer we get closer to the heart of it all, to the very truth about life, and at the centre is the soul. But the Russians come here in their tanks and they say hand over that gift of yours, comrade. We'll take care of it for you. Hands off. Don't peel off the wrappings. Don't ask questions. We'll tell you what the truth is. And if you say no, I'd rather find out for myself, they stick a pistol in your neck and pull the trigger and that's the end of your gift. And if you say yes and hand it over, that's the end of your gift, too. So all you can do is fight if you're eleven years old or if you're a hundred. Otherwise they'll nail you up in your coffin without waiting for you to be dead.

BORBALA My God, you do go on. Listen, all I want is my brother. I'm not interested in his soul. All I want is his body. He's my brother. I brought him up because my mother was always sick. I changed his nappies for him and you can't get closer to anybody than that. Such an ugly little baby, too, but he was my brother. Wouldn't do a thing I told him, but he was my brother. You know what? He wouldn't be kissed on the lips –never. When you put him to bed you had to kiss him on the leg – yes, the leg! Then he'd say, 'Now Laszlo's 'nother leg. Kiss Laszlo's 'nother leg.' And so I'd have to kiss both his legs goodnight. I did that for years –kissed his legs goodnight. The next time I get hold of him I'll break them both for him. Don't you understand? He's my brother! Have you no brothers of your own? [*Pause*] Well, have you?

JOSZEF I . . . well . . .

BORBALA Come on, either you have or you haven't.

JOSZEF I had . . . a sister.

BORBALA You had? Had? [*Pause*] Oh no. How old was she?

JOSZEF Nineteen.

BORBALA Dear God. When did . . .

JOSZEF Just a little while ago.

BORBALA Precious Jesus. [*She crosses herself*] Well, she's in Heaven, you can be sure of that.

JOSZEF My father, too.

BORBALA Dear God. Were they together?

JOSZEF Yes, they were together. I must let my mother know somehow.

BORBALA She doesn't know? Why aren't you at home with her? [*He shakes his head in bewilderment*] You can't face her? No, you'd rather face the tanks. It's easier. Look, I'm sorry. I can see how you're suffering. My mother's suffering, too. If you know anything, please help me to put her mind at rest. Tell me he's alive and I'll go. I give you my word of honour. I'll walk out of here without saying another word. [*Pause*] Well?

JOSZEF He's alive.

BORBALA [*A whisper*] What?
JOSZEF He's alive and well.
BORBALA Where is he?
JOSZEF What?
BORBALA Where is my brother?
BORBALA That wasn't part of our bargain.
BORBALA Bargain? Bargain? Do you think I make bargains with my brother's life? [*Her eyes dart about the room*] Where is he? Laszlo? Answer me this minute or I'll give you such a good hiding. [*She strides about the room, opening cupboards, tipping over furniture, and so on, saying as she does so*] Laszlo! Laszlo! Do you hear? Your mother's fading away before my eyes. She hasn't eaten a crumb in four nights. Laszlo, you're killing your mother, you little swine! [*She stands in the middle of the room in frustration. She changes her tune to a tender one*] Laszlo? Laszlo, darling? Cross my heart, if you come out now I won't touch a hair of your head.
JOSZEF And we all know how she keeps her word.
BORBALA Shut up, you. [*Her glance comes to rest on the beer barrel. She goes up to it and finds the violin case*] So. Not here. [*She places a chair beside the barrel and stands on it to remove the rifles from the tea-chest on top, then pushes the tea-chest on to the floor. She draws the blanket slowly from the barrel and stares down into the depths for a long moment. Then she thrusts her arm inside and brings it out gripping* LASZLO *by the hair*] Come on! Out! Out! My God, you stink like a brewery. Yes, you'll probably die of drink if I can keep you alive long enough.
LASZLO [*Caught by the hair – giving an occasional cry of pain*] Comrade, you gave me your promise. Ow! You've given me away to the enemy. Look, she's killing me! Ow! Why are you just standing there?
JOSZEF What can I do?

LASZLO You've got a gun, haven't you?
JOSZEF You want me to blow her brains out?
LASZLO Yes, what are you waiting for?
JOSZEF What if I hit you instead?
LASZLO I don't care. I'll be out of her clutches for ever.
BORBALA Out of my clutches! My God, I've kept you alive from the age of nil! [*She shakes his head from side to side and slaps his face.*]
JOSZEF Stop! Don't go and spoil it all by killing him at the age of eleven.
LASZLO [*In tears*] Honestly, Borbala! Please, Borbala, let me stay! I won't get killed. That's a promise. We're winning, we're winning!
BORBALA Winning? It's all over, you little fool. The Russians are mopping up. Ask him. [*To* JOSZEF] Well go on. Tell him. You've lost, haven't you? Yes, and what have you achieved? [*Pause*] Well?
JOSZEF They'll treat us with more respect after this. A wise man doesn't stamp on a wasps' nest. [*Pause, then he cocks his head on one side and listens. A motorcycle has stopped with its engine running in the street below*] Quiet, quiet. [*He stands at the side of the window and glances down into the street.* LASZLO *climbs out of the barrel.* JOSZEF *comes back to the others*] A bike. Russian patrol. Driver and machine-gunner.
BORBALA My God, what on earth's going to happen to my mother if I . . .
JOSZEF Hush. Don't worry. Just a routine patrol.

LASZLO *grabs a rifle, runs to the window and aims down into the street. Before he can shoot* JOSZEF *brings him crashing to the floor and they lie there until the motorcycle revs up and drives away. They stand.*

JOSZEF Idiot! Cretin! Did they see you?
LASZLO I could have got them both! I had the driver in my sights. Then the gunner would have been a sitting –
JOSZEF I said did they see you?
LASZLO I don't know! How should I know!
JOSZEF Idiot! You want the entire Red Army charging down this street? You know what they do to a house with a sniper inside? They bring up the tanks and blast it to rubble. Do you never think?
BORBALA Leave him alone! Did you ever think at eleven years old? That's what I've been trying to hammer into your skull. He still thinks he's playing with pop-guns. [*Grabbing* LASZLO] Now come on, we're going home.
LASZLO [*Resisting*] But honestly, we're winning! I'd be a deserter!
BORBALA Winning! Oh, my God!
LASZLO We are! We're winning! I saw seven of their tanks burning in the street this morning.
BORBALA Seven? I suppose you thought that was wonderful. [*She turns her back on him and addresses her next remarks to* JOSZEF . *As she does the rumble of a tank is heard in the distance and* LASZLO *goes to the window and looks out*] How many Red Army boys to a tank? Three? That's twenty-one mothers weeping in Russia. And for what? Nothing of any use that I can see. [LASZLO *stealthily steals two Molotov cocktails from the table and slips through the door unobserved*] I spoke to one of their soldiers in Parliament Square this morning. He was about as old as you. He was totally bewildered. He thought he was in Berlin fighting the Fascists. It's just . . . pitiable. They're dying in droves and they don't even know where they are or who they're fighting – like

blind boys who've wandered into a swarm of bees. [JOSZEF *suddenly hears the tank and goes to the window*] What is it?

JOSZEF A tank at the end of the street.

BORBALA A tank? [*Glancing about*] Laszlo? Laszlo!

She starts for the door.

JOSZEF It's too late. He's there. He's out there skating towards the tank.

BORBALA [*Rushing to join him*] My God, now it's the end! Laszlo! [*They both stare out. Suddenly she clutches her ears. There is the sound of an explosion*] What happened? I can't see a thing. Did he get away?

JOSZEF God knows. All I can see is fire and black smoke.

BORBALA He got away. Pray God he did. Yes, I know he did. He gets away with everything. Just wait till I get hold of him. [*She hurries to the door and opens it, then stops*] Well, are you coming – before they bring another tank up? No, you're going to stay here and fight the tanks single-handed. Oh, that will be highly romantic, won't it? And completely useless. [*Pause*] All right, goodbye.

JOSZEF Wait, stop. [*He selects two rifles, slings one over his shoulder and hands the other to her*] We might need them. Now come on.

BORBALA *does not want a rifle. She calmly leans it up against the wall. She puts an arm round* JOSZEF'S *waist and his arm over her shoulder and helps him to hobble out of the room. The door closes. There is a distant rumble of heavy gun-fire.*

NUTS
PETER TERSON

Characters

DAD	
MUM	
TRACEY	Their daughter
ROBBIE	Their son

I owe the idea of this play to Arnold Wesker, a playwright who I much admire. When I was compiling this anthology I wrote to him from Barcelona, asking him to write a play, and I promised him a bag of nuts in return.

When I came home he was ready to start a play for me but he complained vigorously that I hadn't brought his nuts, so I wrote this by way of reparation.

Although it might seem to be a slight way to treat family relationships, I know that mighty rocks have been split by tiny cracks, and each family has tiny fissures beneath the surface.

DAD has been to Barcelona on a business trip and returns with presents. But he has forgotten his son's nuts.

[TRACEY *is doing a flamenco dance with loud 'Holés'. Enter* ROBBIE, *her younger brother.*]

ROBBIE What are you doing?
TRACEY A flamenco dance, Holé.
ROBBIE What's that in aid of?
TRACEY Dad's due back from Barcelona.
ROBBIE So what?
TRACEY He's promised to bring me a flamenco skirt and a pair of castanets. Holé.

[*She dances.*]

TRACEY What's he promised to bring you?
ROBBIE A bag of nuts!
TRACEY Is that all?
ROBBIE It's all I wanted.
TRACEY Nuts!
ROBBIE Barcelona is famous for its nuts, not flipping flamenco and flaming castanets.
TRACEY All of Spain is famous for its flamenco and castanets.
ROBBIE That's tourist Spain. Barcelona has a thriving nut industry.
TRACEY Nuts to you.
ROBBIE That's the extent of your argument.

[ROBBIE *goes.*
Enter MUM.]

MUM What are you doing Trace?
TRACEY Flamenco dancing, Holé.
MUM Very nice. Why?
TRACEY Dad's due back from Barcelona isn't he? He's promised me a flamenco skirt and a pair of castanets.

MUM Tracey love, you won't be disappointed if he doesn't bring them?
TRACEY Of course he'll bring them.
MUM But you won't be disappointed if he doesn't?
TRACEY Don't be such a wet blanket, Mum.
MUM I don't want to be a wet blanket, but Tracey, stop a minute Tracey. Pay attention, listen to what I have to say for just a minute. You see, Dad's business is a *little* uncertain at the moment.
TRACEY He's *hard up*!
MUM No, I didn't say that.
TRACEY He's going bust.
MUM Don't be alarmed. But let's say there has been pressure on him. He's gone out to Spain to win a contract; if he *does* win it, all well and good, if he doesn't . . . then he could be in difficulty.
TRACEY But he promised me a flamenco skirt and a pair of castanets.
MUM You know your Dad; he's full of promises when the sun is shining.
TRACEY You *are* a wet blanket mum.
MUM I'm not, I'm just practical.

[*Enter* ROBBIE.]

ROBBIE Dad's coming.
MUM Don't rush out. Let's just sit here. Pretend we don't know he's here. He loves taking us by surprise . . .

[*They sit.*]

TRACEY I can hardly contain my excitement.
MUM Just try.

[*Enter* DAD *wrapped in Spanish gear.*]

DAD Señora, Señorita . . . bambino . . . la la la . . . holé.
MUM Darling. Welcome back.
TRACEY Dad!

[DAD *struts proudly.*]

DAD And now, my Señora, my bambino . . . presents from Sunny Spain. To you, my Señora . . . a silk mantilla á la VELASQUEZ . . .
MUM Oh George.
DAD And my Señorita . . . my little one . . . a flamenco skirt and a pair of castanets.
TRACEY Oh Dad, Dad, can I put it on?
DAD Presto my bambino.

[*She rushes off.*]

DAD And for you my proud boy . . . a sombrero and poncho . . .
ROBBIE Where are my nuts?
DAD Nuts?
ROBBIE You promised me a packet of Barcelona nuts.
DAD But look, a poncho, a sombrero . . .
ROBBIE I wanted nuts.
DAD For the price of the poncho and the sombrero I could have brought you a shipload of nuts.
ROBBIE I didn't want a shipload, I wanted a packet.
DAD Well, you didn't get nuts, you got a sombrero, and a poncho.

ROBBIE That's the worst of you, you make promises that you never keep.

[*He goes.*]

DAD [*Aghast*] Did you hear that! I make promises I never keep.

MUM Never mind dear. He'll forget it. You did alright I take it? In business?

DAD I swung it. Yes. The contract is mine . . . It just needs signing and presto . . . He said I make promises I never keep!

MUM Well, there's a certain amount of truth in it.

DAD Truth in it . . . truth . . . me make promises I never keep?

MUM Well, a little bit of truth.

DAD Name it . . . name me *one time* that I never kept a promise I made to my children . . .

MUM That time I went into hospital . . .

DAD Yes?

MUM You promised to take them camping up Snowdon and you ended up in a boarding-house in Tenby.

DAD Bloody hell . . . South Wales instead of North Wales, do you call *that* breaking a promise?

MUM It was to them.

DAD It *tipped* down in North Wales that year, but it was beautiful in Tenby.

MUM You didn't promise them the weather, you promised them the place.

DAD It was more of a *diversion* than a broken promise.

TRACEY [*Off*] Are you ready?

DAD In a minute. Wait for your Caballero . . . [*to* MUM] She's satisfied.

MUM She got what she was promised. He was promised nuts.

DAD Nuts. I could go down to the supermarket and get him a packet of nuts.

MUM That wouldn't be the same, he wanted nuts from Barcelona.

DAD The supermarket nuts are from Barcelona . . . Ninety per cent of our nut supply comes from Barcelona . . .

TRACEY Ready Caballero?

DAD [*Putting on hat*] Ready Señorita Chico . . .

[TRACEY *comes in and they do a flamenco routine.* ROBBIE *slips in.*]

MUM Are you alright?

ROBBIE Yeah.

MUM Sure you're alright?

ROBBIE Yeah.

MUM You're not wearing your nice things.

ROBBIE No.

MUM You *are* alright, tell me you're alright?

TRACEY [*Irritated by the distraction*] Mum, are you *watching* Mum?

MUM Oh yes dear, very nice dear, go on.

[TRACEY *and* DAD *continue their routine.*]

MUM You're *sure* you're alright then?

ROBBIE Yeah.

MUM Why not wear your things then?

ROBBIE Don't want to.

MUM Please.

ROBBIE No.

MUM For me then? For mum?
ROBBIE Don't want to.
MUM I'm looking appealing.
TRACEY [*Stopping*] You're spoiling it aren't you?
ROBBIE I'm not.
TRACEY You're just trying to spoil it.
ROBBIE I'm not.
TRACEY You're just trying to get attention for yourself.
ROBBIE I'm not.
TRACEY You always try to get attention for yourself.
ROBBIE I don't.
TRACEY You do.
ROBBIE When? Name me a time. When?
TRACEY That time in Tenby, when Dad entered me for the talent competition; I was half way through my routine when you pretended to be sick.
ROBBIE I didn't pretend to be sick.
TRACEY You did.
ROBBIE I didn't. I *was* sick . . . That routine of yours made me sick. That Shirley Temple stuff . . . [*Mimicking*] On the good ship, *Lollipop*.
TRACEY Yaaaah . . . [*Flies off*]
DAD Tracey!
MUM Let her go, I'll go up later.
DAD [*To* ROBBIE] Now look what you've done.
ROBBIE What have I done?
DAD Don't play the innocent with me you cunning little brat.
MUM Dad, stop it.
DAD I came back hoping for a little party . . . and you spoil it . . . why?
ROBBIE You promised me nuts.
DAD It wasn't the nuts. You just used the nuts as an excuse to ruin my homecoming . . . As always.
ROBBIE As always?

DAD Yes, as always . . .
MUM Dad, you're saying too much.
DAD I know what I'm saying . . . He was exactly the same in Tenby. Exactly the same . . . The weather was lovely, we had a nice boarding-house. I planned to play rounders on the sand, go on cliff walks but he sulked.
ROBBIE You promised to take us to Snowdon.
DAD But we went to Tenby, you might have tried to enjoy Tenby. But you ruined it, by sulking.
ROBBIE I didn't sulk, I was just quiet. I didn't want to do it *your way*. You want it *all* your own way don't you? So long as it's going *your* way life is fine. But I don't want it *your* way thanks.
DAD [*Angrily*] So long as I'm the wage-earner in this family you *will do things my way*.
ROBBIE Right, great, we know where we stand . . . what a democracy.

[*He goes.*]

MUM Leave him. I'll go up afterwards.
DAD What a homecoming. I plan for a great return, I imagine how it could be, I try to arrange it to make us all happy . . . then flop . . . Just like Tenby.
MUM Tenby wasn't your fault dear.
DAD But this is!
MUM It's just a pity you forgot the nuts.
DAD The nuts. They never crossed my mind, the damned nuts. I saw the sombrero, I saw the poncho . . . I thought of Robbie like Clint Eastwood . . . Nuts were driven from my mind.
MUM I'll go and see if Tracey's alright now.
DAD Stella.

MUM Yes.
DAD Shall I go down to the supermarket and get some nuts?
MUM I don't think so.
DAD I could pretend I'd left them in the car by mistake.
MUM I don't think that would work.
DAD Stella?
MUM Yes?
DAD You like your mantilla alright don't you?
MUM Very nice dear . . . but I don't know on what sort of occasion I'll wear it.

She goes.

DAD *gets out his duty-free and pours a glass of his Spanish brandy. He then lights his cigar.*

Enter ROBBIE *dressed as Clint Eastwood.*

ROBBIE [*Sinister*] Have you ever imagined what you look like?
DAD Eh? Oh Robbie, that's good.
ROBBIE Stay where you are . . . unless you want a fistful.
DAD Of dollars?
ROBBIE Of teeth. Git them hands up.
DAD Sure Robbie . . . hey what an act.
ROBBIE If you take two paces back, bend them weak knees your butt will contact a chair.
DAD Sure Robbie. Sure, want any music . . .
ROBBIE I'll provide the music round here.

ROBBIE *takes his cigar.*

ROBBIE You had mouth contact with this?
DAD I was just about to start when . . .

[ROBBIE *bites the end off and spits it out.*]

DAD Hi, Mum's carpet.
ROBBIE Make my day and move.

[*Takes brandy bottle.*]

A good brand eh?
DAD Not bad, ha, in fact, pretty good. Yeah, now don't drink that stuff hombre.
ROBBIE You musta clinched a good deal eh?
DAD Not bad, not bad at all.
ROBBIE Do you know it kinda makes me sick the way you crawl around to clinch your little deals.
DAD Hi, steady on now Rob. Steady on.
ROBBIE You get a little tickle then you come back here like you're Christ Almighty Big Shot. Loaded up with trinkets, a mediocre bottle of brandy, pulp cigars to foul the atmosphere. It makes me really puke, you know that? You want us to play your little game, well hear this, your little game is over.
DAD Now listen here you . . .
ROBBIE Just rise and you're dead. I've seen through you buddy. Since I was so high I've wised up to you. You haven't got a grain of grit in you. You're transparent as a pool, empty as a desert and prickly as a cactus. The only flower in your landscape is your family and you're walking all over it . . .

[DAD *jumps up and grabs him.*
Enter MUM.]

MUM George . . . are you alright Rob? You alright?
DAD Just playing Rob's game.
MUM Game?
DAD Yeah, he was good too. Didn't know he was an actor. I thought Tracey was the actor. But he gets into a part real well.

[ROBBIE *drops his gear on the floor and walks out.*]

DAD See you hombre . . . Ain't you sticking around? That boy doesn't know how to show affection to me.
MUM Doesn't he?
DAD That's his problem. Basic sense of inadequacy.
MUM Who does he feel inadequate to?
DAD Me of course. Me. I've seen it. Seen it for years. All this fuss over the nuts is a sign. Inadequacy. Pure tantrums.
MUM Perhaps he just wanted the nuts.
DAD Nuts is about as big a concept as he can hold in his head. He's got a nut-sized brain.
MUM His exam results came while you were away.
DAD What did they come in? A pill-box?
MUM He did extremely well.
DAD What in?
MUM In everything, especially languages. French, German, Spanish . . . they think he'll be a linguist. He can ask for nuts in Spanish, which is more than you can do.

DAD I can ask for nuts in Spanish.
MUM What is it?

[DAD *points. Mimes cracking a nut.*]

MUM That's not asking . . . that's just your own method.
DAD Well let me tell you, my method in life gets results. I've built up my own company, I've got a European subsidiary and I've just swung a big contract in Spain. Let him top that!
MUM If you'd get off his back I think he could.
DAD What do you mean? Get off his back. What do you mean, exactly. Get off his back, I'd like you to tell me what that implies.
MUM I think you've tended to Lord it over him with your own achievements.
DAD Fathers have a responsibility to set their sons an example.
MUM But not to sit on them.
DAD When did I *ever* sit on him? I'd like to know that. Give me *one example* when I've sat on him.
MUM That time at Tenby, in the chess tournament you sat at his elbow whispering instructions.
DAD I wanted him to get into the second round.
MUM *You* were knocked out in the first round.
DAD That was in the Senior section.
MUM I'll go and see how he is.
DAD Pining for his nuts.

[*Exit* MUM.
Enter TRACEY.]

DAD And here is my little girl . . . Señorita . . . are you going to put on your skirt eh, and you and I will go into a flamenco? – I'm taking up the guitar you know so you and I can be partners in the flamenco . . . Manitas de Plata . . .

[*Sings flamenco . . .*]

La la da dum . . .

[*Puts his arms round his daughter's waist.*]

TRACEY Don't do that Dad . . . Dad, leave me . . . [*Struggles free*] You're just always handling people . . .

DAD You, my daughter.

TRACEY Oh, anybody, any woman.

DAD Me . . .

TRACEY You're not even aware you do it.

DAD Obviously not.

TRACEY Away from Mum you're not safe to be out . . .

DAD Since when has this absurd observation been extant?

TRACEY You were like that at Tenby.

DAD Tenby.

TRACEY You were disgusting at Tenby. And Mum in hospital. Ogling and handling every woman present.

DAD Me!

TRACEY It was absolutely nauseating.

DAD Tracey, Tracey . . .

[*Touches her.*]

TRACEY Please don't handle me . . .
DAD I'm your father.
TRACEY I don't like being pawed.
DAD Pawed! It was different when I brought you back your flamenco skirt and castanets . . .
TRACEY Buying love. You were always good at that. Keep your flamenco skirt and castanets. I'd rather have had a packet of nuts than be pawed by you.

[*Drops her gear and stalks out.*
DAD *aghast.*
Enter MUM.]

MUM He's locked himself in his room. But I think he's alright. I called him and he mumbled something about south of the Sierra Grande. So I left him.
DAD Tracey left her flamenco skirt and castanets.
MUM Robbie has left his poncho and sombrero.
DAD Gratitude.
MUM Oh, you don't understand.
DAD About what?
MUM Tracey, Robbie . . . the nuts.
DAD You do, I suppose.
MUM I think I do.
DAD Because you're always conniving with them.
MUM They talk with me.
DAD They never talk to me.
MUM I'm more their confidante.
DAD You're always whispering to them. Behind closed doors.
MUM They can be intimate with me.
DAD Mumbling, conspiring, ganging up against me.
MUM No.
DAD I'm on my own in this house. I can see it now. Father. That's a laugh. Wage-earner I am. I'm a

stranger in my own household . . . If they don't like my presents, I'll keep my presents. I like my presents. I'm happy enough with them. I can have fun. Complete loner in my own family. Isolated. You've isolated me you lot, I can see that. I wish I'd never got married. I do . . .

MUM George.

DAD I do. I was young. I never loved you. Just slipped into marriage like a blinkered racehorse . . . Try to make it up by loving the kids . . . they don't respond, don't reciprocate . . . well go to them, go to them, see what I care . . .

MUM George.

[*She rushes out. He picks up the presents one by one and wears them.*]

DAD I don't care. I like my presents. I can have fun. I don't need them. I don't need you lot . . . do you hear? I don't need *you lot* . . . .

[*Dances flamenco.*]

WAITING FOR THE PARTY

MARY CUTLER

Characters

SUSIE
JANE
GEM
DARREN
JIM
MICK

'Where do you get your ideas from?' is one of the questions writers are often asked, to which a totally honest reply would often be 'I wish I knew.' When the phone rang one Sunday morning, and a cheery voice asked 'Would you like to write a play for young people? No toilets, no suicides, no social workers, but apart from that you can do what you like,' I was presented with a golden opportunity to work out where my ideas did come from because at that particular moment, I didn't have any.

First, I wanted to write something that would be interesting to perform and to watch. What interests young people, I wondered. Each other, so there was my theme: relationships between the sexes. Then, I needed a place for them to meet: a party was the obvious setting. Then, there were the characters: in a short play these couldn't be too many, or too complex. I remember someone telling me you knew you'd stopped just writing dialogue and started writing a play when you could manage three people in a scene, so I picked three girls and three boys, three potential couples; easily recognisable types, perhaps, but I think in adolescence more than any other time we find ourselves playing roles that don't quite fit our personalities.

[*The scenes to begin with alternate between the girls in* SUSIE*'s living-room, and the boys hanging round their street corner. It would be possible, therefore, for these to be set either end of the stage and the boys to be mooching about while the girls talk, and the girls to be preparing for the party while the boys talk. Alternatively the relevant scene could just be spotlighted.*]

Scene 1

[SUSIE's *living-room.*
SUSIE *and* JANE *and* GEM *are looking round it eyeing up the possibilities.*]

SUSIE Mum says we've got to stay in here.
JANE What, all night? Can't we even go in the kitchen? Where are we going to put the drinks?
GEM It's quite a big room.
SUSIE What drinks?
JANE What drinks – what drinks? You mean we aren't supposed to be having any drinks, either?
SUSIE She's not buying it. And I haven't got any money.

JANE Oh well, we'll just have to make sure everyone brings a bottle.

GEM Will that be alright with your Mum?

SUSIE Oh yes. It's just she hasn't got any money either.

JANE The boys will bring some. I suppose we are going to be able to bring boys?

SUSIE Oh, yes. Only –

GEM I don't know any.

JANE Only what?

SUSIE Only she doesn't want us to go in the bedrooms.

JANE Oh, God. Oh, well, I suppose this carpet's quite soft. [*She feels it*]

GEM Does it matter? That I don't know any?

SUSIE Oh, no. Jane know lots – she'll lend you one, won't you, Jane?

JANE [*Bouncing on settee*] I suppose this'll do. What?

SUSIE You'll lend Gem one of your spare admirers.

JANE Oh, yes. You could have Darren. Or Mick. Just keep your paws off Jim.

SUSIE Jim? You don't fancy Jim, do you?

GEM Jim Evans? Is he coming?

JANE Everyone fancies Jim. Everyone in their right mind.

SUSIE Right mind, lousy eyesight. What about his spots?

JANE They've nearly all gone now.
Well, what Superman have you got your eye on, then?

SUSIE Nobody in particular. I'm the hostess – I can have anybody –

GEM What are Darren and Mick like?

JANE You can't have Jim.

SUSIE I don't want Jim. Mick's nice.

GEM Oh. Is he the one you –

JANE He's a wimp. And if we're talking about spots –
SUSIE He's alright. Just because he's not all mouth and trousers like Jim.
JANE No, I've never heard him open his mouth. And as for his trousers –
SUSIE He's alright. He grows on you.
GEM What's Darren like?
JANE I should think something very nasty might grow on you if you went anywhere near him.
SUSIE Well, don't go anywhere near him then. You stick to Jim and I'll stick to Mick.
JANE Suits me.
GEM Do you think Darren will like me?

Scene 2

[*A street corner.*
JIM, DARREN *and* MICK *are hanging about it, throwing stones, kicking tin cans, etc.*]

DARREN You going to this party tonight?
JIM What party is this?
MICK Susie's party. Are you going?
DARREN I might. If nothing better turns up.
JIM Is that the one Jane keeps on about?
MICK Must be. I thought I might give it a go.
DARREN Oh, well, if Jane's asked you –
JIM If Jane's asked me what?
DARREN [*Imitating*] Oh, Jim, darling, do come to the party. [*Flutters eyelashes*] I want you so much.
JIM I can't help being irresistible to women, mate.
MICK She's alright, Jane.
DARREN Always good for a neck, I'll say that for her.
JIM How would you know?

DARREN I've been to parties with Jane.

JIM Yeah, and I've been to parties with you. You usually spend the first hour getting paralytic and the rest of the time throwing up.

MICK There's no drink.

DARREN No drink? No drink? Oh, well that's it then. I'm not going.

JIM You're joking.

MICK Not provided. You've got to bring your own.

DARREN No drink.

JIM Well, that's alright then, Darren. I'm sure you've got the odd crate going spare, haven't you?

MICK I quite fancy going.

DARREN You quite fancy Susie.

JIM Susie, Susie, don't be choosey . . .

MICK She's a nice girl. She grows on you.

DARREN Here, hang on a minute. I've been thinking.

MICK Oh, blimey. Ring the *Guinness Book of Records*.

DARREN You two are fixed up. What about me?

MICK You've got your crate of lager.

JIM There's bound to be loads of girls there. Some of them might be desperate.

DARREN Oh no, I want one fixed up. I know those girls – they just sit in a corner giggling and talking to each other.

MICK You want to try talking back. Works wonders.

JIM They've got that friend – what's her name – Gem – she'd do.

DARREN Gem? Gem? What kind of a name is that?

Scene 3

The living-room.
Now all ready for the party. The girls are dressed-up and made-up. They stand in a line facing the audience.

JANE I've washed my hair.
SUSIE I've had a bath.
GEM With bubbles in.
JANE I've shaved my legs.
SUSIE I've done my nails.
GEM I've squeezed my spots.
JANE I've found some clean knickers.
SUSIE And a clean bra.
GEM And a pair of new tights.
JANE I put on one dress.
SUSIE And then another.
GEM And then a skirt and top.
JANE/SUSIE/GEM Because none of them looked right.
JANE Because tonight I want to look stunning.
SUSIE Smashing.
GEM Sensational.
JANE I want to be the star of the show.
SUSIE The belle of the ball.
GEM I want it to go right this time.
JANE This time.
SUSIE This time.
GEM This time.
JANE This time I'll get him.
SUSIE This time he'll get me.
GEM This time something will happen.
JANE This time.
SUSIE This time.
GEM This time.

JANE/SUSIE/GEM It'll all be all right. This time. [*They look at the boys*] We're ready.
MICK Shall we go then? To this party?
JIM Might as well, I suppose.
DARREN Nothing much better to do is there?

[*They mooch off. Blackout.*]

Scene 4

[*The living-room.*
The girls are all dressed up for the party and putting final touches to the room.]

GEM What time did you tell them?
SUSIE Eight o'clock.
JANE They'll be here about nine then.
GEM Really? But I told my Mum I'd be home for eleven.
SUSIE You can stay the night if you like.
JANE You can get a lot done in two hours, you know. Can I try the music?
GEM Thanks. Well, I'll see how it goes.
SUSIE I'll do it – our stereo's a bit tricky if you're not used to it.

[*She puts the tape on.*]

JANE Can't we have it louder than that?
SUSIE No. The old bag next door will complain.
GEM Shall I turn it down a bit?

JANE No. You can hardly hear it as it is.
SUSIE She called the police at half past nine last time we had a party.
GEM She didn't. How awful.
JANE Why, what were you doing?
SUSIE Nothing. Nothing at all. There was hardly anyone here.
JANE There's hardly anyone here now.
GEM Did they come?
SUSIE Yes.
GEM What did they say?
SUSIE Keep the noise down a bit, bab.
GEM And your Mum let you have another party?
SUSIE It was my Mum's party last time.
JANE Come on, let's dance. I'm bored.
SUSIE Go on, then.
GEM What, with each other?
JANE Well, I can't do it on my own.

Scene 5

The boys are walking towards the party. MICK *is anxious to get there.* DARREN *has stopped to drink from a bottle.* JIM *is eyeing him.*

MICK Oh do get a move on you two. Darren, can't you wait till we get there?
DARREN No. [*Takes another swig.*]
JIM Steady on. There'll be nothing left.
MICK Jim, Jane's waiting for you.
JIM [*Indifferent*] Oh yeah. Come on, Daz. It's my turn now.
DARREN What do you mean your turn? This is my bottle.

MICK Come on.
JIM No, it's not.
DARREN Yes, it is. I bought it.
MICK Oh, for God's sake.
JIM No, you didn't. I bought it. I gave it you to carry and –
MICK You drink too much anyway.
DARREN Don't.
JIM Do.
MICK Why do you drink so much?
DARREN What else is there to do?
JIM Dutch courage.
MICK We could go to this party.
JIM He can't talk to girls unless he's half sloshed. And with the lovely Gem waiting for him –

[DARREN *is drinking throughout this.*]

MICK If she is waiting. If we don't get a move on they'll all have gone home.
JIM You're alright, Susie lives there.
MICK She's had time to move while I've been hanging about waiting for you two.
JIM Don't get your Y-fronts in a twist. They'll wait. We're worth waiting for.
MICK Jane might think you are, but Susie's got a bit more –
DARREN Are you two going to stand here arguing over women all night? I've finished the bottle. Come on.

Scene 6

[SUSIE's *house.*
JANE *is twitching quietly to the music.* GEM *is eating her way through a plate of sandwiches.*]

SUSIE Gem! There won't be anything to eat by the time they get here.
GEM Sorry. I always eat when I'm nervous. What time do you think they will get here?
JANE Nine o'clock, I told you. And they won't be interested in food.
SUSIE You've got a one-track mind.
GEM You've had a lot of experience, haven't you, Jane?

[SUSIE *chokes on a crisp.*]

JANE I know my way around.
SUSIE Round the bike sheds, the bus shelters, the back of the Odeon –
GEM I wish I did.
JANE I'm not easy, though.
SUSIE No, Jane, of course you're not.
GEM I wish I was.
SUSIE/JANE [*Shocked*] Gem!
GEM Oh not like that. I mean – I wish I found things easy – with boys.
JANE Nothing to it.
SUSIE Nothing to them – most of the time.
GEM I don't know – it seems like – everyone else knows what to do – and I don't –
JANE It's not complicated.
SUSIE Just be yourself.

GEM That's what I mean. It's so obvious to you you can't explain it – and I can't see it.
JANE Nothing to see. Look, suppose you want to get off with Darren.
SUSIE I don't know, Gem, you might be better off as you are.
GEM But I don't know him.
JANE Well, you will after you've got off with him, won't you?
SUSIE That's the best bit. Before you know them.
JANE Look, I'll be Darren – you practise on me.
GEM Practise?
SUSIE Jane! All the years we've been friends and you never told me.
JANE Practise chatting me up. Go on.

[JANE *assumes bored* DARREN-*like look,* SUSIE *giggles.*]

GEM But – you're not saying anything.
JANE Well, I wouldn't be would I? If I was Darren?
SUSIE You're sure you want to go on with this Gem? You're probably better off with a nice book.
JANE Oh, that's what you're going to do with Mick is it? Read to him? Come on, give the girl a chance.
GEM Right. Hello, my name's Gem.
JANE Funny name.
GEM Um? It's short for Gemma.
JANE Oh yeah?
GEM It means jewel.
JANE Is that right. [*Silence*]
JANE Go on.
GEM I can't think of anything else to say.

SUSIE A good book – exercise classes – learn a language.

JANE You shut up. Oh, come on, Gem, you're not trying. You don't even know his name yet, do you?

GEM Oh – right – er – what's yours?

JANE Darren.

GEM Oh yes. You're a friend of Mick's aren't you? And Jim's.

JANE Call them friends? Nick all me booze and then desert me.

SUSIE [*Laughing*] You're very good at this.

JANE Sh! Yes. Absolutely gasping I am.

GEM Oh dear.

JANE For a drink. And being a stranger in the house –

GEM Yes, it must be very . . . [JANE *pantomimes fetching drink*] Oh, would you like me to find you one?

JANE Yes. Thanks. [*As herself*] Well go on then.

GEM You mean you really want one. You, Jane.

SUSIE Me Tarzan. You could try that one Gem –

JANE Yes. Me Jane. After that lot I think I deserve one.

Scene 7

The boys have at last reached SUSIE*'s street.*

JIM What number did you say it was?

MICK Forty two.

DARREN This is thirty eight.

JIM Must be the one with the purple door. Here I come Jane. You're luck's in tonight.

MICK I hope she thinks so.

JIM I haven't had any complaints yet.

MICK You never stick around long enough to hear them.

DARREN I hope the drink hasn't run out.

MICK Wham, bam, thank you ma'am.
JIM Oh yeah? And I suppose all you're hoping to get out of Susie tonight is a bit of intelligent conversation.
MICK Yes.
DARREN Oh, come on. Otherwise none of us are going to get anything.

Scene 8

SUSIE's house.
The girls are sitting staring into space gloomily.

SUSIE They're not coming, are they?
JANE Course they are.
GEM It's only – half past nine.
SUSIE I knew no one would come.
JANE I didn't. Or I wouldn't have come myself.
GEM Well. We're here. We can still have a good time. Without the boys.
JANE Oh yeah, great.
GEM You said we could, Susie. You said they weren't worth it.
SUSIE I said Darren wasn't. I didn't think Mick would let me down.
JANE Oh, I thought Jim might. But I'd have made do with somebody else.
GEM I don't mind, Susie.
SUSIE Thank you, Gem.
JANE I do.
SUSIE Yes, thanks Jane. Times like this you find out who your friends are.

GEM We are all friends. We can enjoy ourselves anyway.
JANE Depends what you want to do.
GEM We can talk. Boys are so difficult to talk to.
SUSIE Yeah that's true. We can have a good old chat, really let our hair down.
JANE I agree they're only useful for one thing but all the same –
SUSIE We don't need them, Jane.
GEM No, we don't.
JANE No. It's their loss.

[*The door bell rings.*]

JANE/SUSIE/GEM [*Big smiles*] They're here!

FUN CITY

BARRY HINES

Characters

TRAVIS	Head teacher
KYLE	Fifth-year boy
SHEARER	P.E. teacher
SECRETARY/FIFTH-YEAR GIRL	

Mr Travis, the head teacher of an inner-city school, is at his wits' end. The building is falling apart through lack of funding. Truancy and vandalism are rife, and members of staff, unable to cope with the pressure, are repeatedly off sick.

Then, to top it all, Mr Shearer, the P.E. teacher, brings Kyle, a fifth-year student to see him, accused of stealing money from the changing-room. Kyle is the last person Travis wants to see. He regards Kyle as a no-hoper, a disastrous failure in educational terms. The antipathy between them is mutual. Kyle regards school as irrelevant and boring. His main interest is out of school; at FUN CITY . . .

Head teacher's study. TRAVIS, *the head teacher, is doing press-ups in his shirt sleeves in the middle of the room. He counts out '18 . . . 19 . . . 20,' then stands up and picks up a stop-*

watch from his desk. He checks it then presses the button and begins running hard on the spot. There is a knock on the door. TRAVIS *continues running, checks the watch, stops it, then puts on his jacket and sits at his desk. He composes himself and picks up a sheet of paper.*

TRAVIS Come in!

There is a pause then KYLE, *a fifth-year boy, makes a reluctant entrance closely followed by* MR SHEARER, *a young P.E. teacher.* SHEARER *is dressed in track suit and trainers,* KYLE *in ripped jeans, worn sneakers, army surplus combat jacket with names of bands felt-tipped on it and a woollen hat.* MR SHEARER *looks agitated, the boy sullen and angry.*

TRAVIS [*Still panting from his exertions*] What is it Mr Shearer?

SHEARER I'd like you to have a word with Kyle if you would Mr Travis. There's been some money stolen from the gym changing-room . . .

KYLE Well it wasn't me! I didn't take it!

SHEARER Of course you did. It couldn't have been anybody else.

KYLE It must have been, 'cos I didn't do it!

TRAVIS Stop shouting lad! Who do you think you're talking to? [*Then to* SHEARER] Can't Mr Franklin deal with this? I'm extremely busy.

SHEARER He's teaching. He's had to fill in for somebody.

TRAVIS Don't tell me someone else is off sick! They're dropping like flies. No stamina, that's the trouble. [*He raises his arms and presses them back three times in a shoulder-stretching exercise*] What about Mrs Sherwood, isn't she available?

SHEARER She's not in school. She's had to take a girl to hospital.

TRAVIS [*Alarmed*] Why, what's happened?

SHEARER A door came off its hinges. She got trapped underneath.

TRAVIS [*Pointing up at the ceiling*] Yes, and I shall be the next casualty. Just look at those cracks. The whole place is falling apart around our ears.

SHEARER What about the showers in the changing-room? Not only is there no hot water; but when a boy turned them on the other day he got an electric shock!

[KYLE *tries hard to suppress a grin at this revelation.*]

TRAVIS Perhaps you should try switching on the lights, see if you get any hot water out of the sockets. [*Pause while he does an isometric exercise, linking his fingers and pulling hard*] It's the cuts. When somebody gets killed, they might call a halt. [*Then, noticing* KYLE *trying to suppress a grin*] What are you smirking at Kyle?

KYLE Nothing sir.

TRAVIS I don't suppose there's much chance of you getting electrocuted in the showers judging by the state of you. And take that hat off. It's not that cold in school.

SHEARER You should come down to the gym. It's like a freezer in there.

TRAVIS Economy Mr Shearer. That's the key word these days. Look at this lot . . . [*He picks up a wad of papers from his desk*] If I took all the reminders I receive from County Hall down to the boiler room, they'd generate enough heat to walk around the school in swimming-trunks.

KYLE *takes off his hat. His head is completely shaven except for a coloured strip of hair down the centre. (Or some other extravagant hair-style.)*

TRAVIS [*Pause, then slowly with great feeling*] Jesus Christ. Who in God's name gave you that?

KYLE [*Puzzled*] What?

TRAVIS That thing! That . . . [*Lost for words*] That abomination on top of your head!

KYLE [*Grinning and stroking his hair proudly*] The hairdressers. Marios in town.

TRAVIS You mean you actually paid to have it done?

KYLE Well he's not going to do it free is he?

SHEARER *keeps his head down, trying hard to conceal his amusement.*

TRAVIS [*Walking round* KYLE *and shaking his head in disbelief*] He should be struck off the register. [*Pause*] And what about your parents? What do they say about it?

KYLE [*Shrugging*] They're not bothered. Anyway, it's my hair.

TRAVIS I'm glad it is lad. If it was mine I'd blow my brains out. And even if your parents approve, I certainly don't. That hair-style is totally unacceptable. I'm trying to run a respectable school here not a freak show.

[TRAVIS *sits down at his desk, puts his palms together in front of his chest and presses until he is red in the face.*]

TRAVIS Now then, tell me what happened Mr Shearer.

SHEARER Well we were out on the field and Kyle said he wanted to go to the toilet.

KYLE You're not blaming me . . .

[*The telephone rings on* TRAVIS'S *desk. He picks it up.*]

TRAVIS Yes . . . They were doing what . . . ? In RE? Good Lord! What were they studying, Genesis . . . ? Well tell them to report to my room at twelve o'clock. I'm busy at the moment. [*He replaces the telephone*] Sodom and Gomorrah in Room 15 by the sound of it. Whatever next? [*Pause*] Sorry about that Mr Shearer, you were saying . . .

SHEARER Well I gave him the key to the changing-room. We carried on with the game and a few minutes later he came back. Then when they were getting changed at the end of the lesson, Weston said that he'd had five pounds stolen out of his pocket.

KYLE Well I didn't take it.

TRAVIS [*Ignoring him*] Are you sure Weston wasn't making it up?

SHEARER No, you could tell. He was genuinely upset. His mother had given it to him to get some shopping on his way home from school.

TRAVIS Perhaps he lost it.

SHEARER He says he checked his pockets before he went out on to the field.

TRAVIS Well it's obvious where it's gone then isn't it? It's an open and shut case.

KYLE I haven't got it.

TRAVIS Who has then? It can't have vanished into thin air.

KYLE How do I know?

TRAVIS Look lad, it's obvious. And I'm telling you, if we don't get that money back I shall turn the matter over to the police.

KYLE [*Pause*] You can do what you like, I didn't take it.

TRAVIS You know what'll happen, don't you, if the police get involved? With your record you could be in serious trouble.

[KYLE *does not answer.*]

SHEARER I've promised him Mr Travis, that if we get the money back it won't go any further. I don't want to see him get into any more trouble and I'm sure you don't.

TRAVIS Of course not.

KYLE How can I when I haven't got it?

SHEARER [*Almost pleading*] Come on, Tony. I'll give it quietly back to Weston and nobody will hear any more about it. All he wants is his money back.

TRAVIS Have you searched him?

SHEARER I made him empty his pockets. But he's hardly going to go walking about with it on him, is he? It could be anywhere?

TRAVIS [*Losing patience*] Kyle! Where is it?

KYLE I've no idea.

TRAVIS Come on lad. It's obvious. It must be you.

KYLE Prove it.

TRAVIS I don't have to prove it. I know! And I'm telling you here and now that you're not leaving this room until I get that money back. I don't care if you've to stay till nine o'clock tonight.

[*There is a pause while* TRAVIS *and* SHEARER *look at* KYLE, *who shows no reaction to this ultimatum.*]

TRAVIS [*Looking at his watch*] You'd better get back to your class Mr Shearer. Just leave him to me now.

[KYLE *and* MR SHEARER *exchange glances, then* MR SHEARER *reluctantly turns to leave.* TRAVIS *gets up from his desk and accompanies him to the door.*]

TRAVIS Don't worry, I'll get it out of him. [*Then, as* SHEARER *opens the door*] By the way, how's the training going?

SHEARER Not bad. I managed ten miles on Sunday.

TRAVIS Clocking up the miles eh? Good man. I don't know how many miles I shall manage on the day, but I shall certainly be doing my best.

SHEARER If all my sponsors cough up, and I don't collapse, I reckon I should raise about twenty pounds.

TRAVIS What a way to run an education service, relying

on gimmicks and the begging bowl. [*He shakes his head despairingly*] Still, keeps us in shape I suppose. It's the survival of the fittest these days.

[SHEARER *leaves the room. Unseen by* KYLE, TRAVIS *does three quick press-ups against the wall, then walks back to his desk and sits down.*]

TRAVIS You'd better sit down lad. It's going to be a long day.

[KYLE *sits down on a chair in front of the desk.*]

TRAVIS I don't suppose you'll be running for SCHOOL AID, Kyle?
KYLE [*Shaking his head*] Why should I?
TRAVIS [*Angrily*] Why should you? It's your school you know! It's for your benefit, not mine!

[*The telephone rings.* TRAVIS *picks it up.*]

TRAVIS Hello . . . Yes. Yes . . . Mothercare! What's she doing there . . . ? Babygros! What's she want them for . . . ? I see. No, I didn't know anything about it . . . Let's hope she gets a good grade in Home Economics . . . Does he intend to prosecute . . . ? Well it's understandable I suppose . . . Would you? I'd be extremely grateful. Tell her to report to her class when she gets back and I'll send for her as soon as I'm free . . . That's right. Sorry to trouble you officer. 'Bye now. [*He replaces the telephone and writes down the girl's name*] Mandy Booth . . . I can't place her. [*Then, savagely, to* KYLE] I'd know who it was if you'd been caught shoplifting. Your file's so thick you've got a drawer in the filing cabinet of your own!

[*Pause. There is no response from* KYLE.]

TRAVIS You're not going to get away with it you know. I'm determined to see this thing through. [*He stands up and walks round the desk*] Look, why don't you make it easy for yourself and own up now? You know what will happen if the police get involved. If you hand it over now you'll hear no more about it.

KYLE How can I when I haven't got it?

TRAVIS You might not have it on you, but you know where it is.

[KYLE *does not reply.*]

TRAVIS Honestly Kyle, I thought you'd have had more sense. Especially at this stage with only a few months to go. It's going to be hard enough finding a job as it is without getting into any more trouble. Who's going to employ somebody with a criminal record when they've the choice of thousands? [*Pause*] I don't understand you Kyle. I don't understand the way your mind works; what makes you tick. I mean, how can you come to school, walk about the streets, be seen in public dressed the way that you are? What sort of career do you think you're going to pursue with hair like that? You know what employers are like. You've got to take these things into consideration Kyle. There's no place for it. You've got to learn to compete. It's a buyer's market, I'm afraid, and there's no way I can sell you to an employer with a hair-style like that.

[*He walks behind* KYLE, *stops and looks down at his head for a few moments in horrified fascination, then picks up a cricket team photograph from his desk. As he looks at the photograph, he places one hand on his hip and begins to rise up and down on his toes.*]

TRAVIS [*More to himself than* KYLE] There was none of this nonsense then . . . What a team that was. Grand bunch of boys. What year was it? [*He peers at the photograph*] Must have been the last of the Grammar School intake. [*He stands still and points to a boy on the photograph*] See him? Martin Blake. He got a scholarship to Oxford.

KYLE I'm going to Oxford. [TRAVIS *looks round at him sharply*] United are playing there next week.

TRAVIS Is that why you stole the money, to go to a football match?

KYLE [*Nearly caught out*] No, I . . . I didn't steal any money!

[*There is a knock on the door.*]

TRAVIS Come in!

[A FIFTH-YEAR GIRL *enters carrying a tray containing a cup of coffee and a plate of biscuits.*]

TRAVIS Thank you Julie. Put them on the desk please.

[JULIE *places the tray on the desk, exchanges glances with* KYLE *and leaves the room. The bell rings for break.*]

TRAVIS [*Picking up the cup*] End of round one. That's what teaching's like today: a boxing match. You're shoved into the ring when the first bell goes, then you stagger from round to round, hoping to remain on your feet until the final bell at four o'clock. [*Pause*] It's a battlefield. You need the fitness of a gladiator to survive.

[KYLE *has not been listening. He stares hungrily at the plate of biscuits.* TRAVIS *picks up a digestive. He holds it up.*]

TRAVIS See that? [*Pause*] 60 calories. [*Pause*] Amazing isn't it? [*He replaces it and picks up a shortbread finger*] How many calories do you think there are in that? [KYLE *does not answer*] Go on. Have a guess. Just guess.

KYLE How do I know?

TRAVIS [*Triumphantly*] 95! And this? [*Picking up a Club Orange. Again* KYLE *does not reply*] 125! Every one a little temptress. Every morning it's a battle of will. [*He replaces the biscuit, shaking his head*] Fatal. Fatal for an athlete. 60, 95, 125. How many calories is that?

[*He picks up a calculator from his desk.*]

KYLE [*Instantly*] 280.

TRAVIS [*Working it out*] Right. Well done. Have a biscuit Kyle. Have two. Have three.

KYLE No thanks.

TRAVIS Why not? I wouldn't think there's much chance of you putting on weight. I've seen more fat on a butcher's pencil.

[TRAVIS *sits down at his desk and swings from side to side in the swivel chair.*]

TRAVIS I don't suppose you're interested in athletics are you, Kyle? [KYLE *does not answer*] Apart from running away from the police of course. That's about the sum total of your sporting career.

[*There is a knock on the door.* TRAVIS *looks annoyed at the interruption.*]

TRAVIS Come in!

[MRS TURNER, *the school secretary, enters the room looking anxious.*]

TRAVIS What is it, Nancy?

MRS TURNER Could I have a word with you, Mr Travis?

TRAVIS Well, I'm rather tied up at the moment. Is it urgent?

MRS TURNER It is rather. It's Mrs Clifford. Jill Clifford's mother. She'd like to see you.

[TRAVIS *can tell from her manner and tone of voice that it is an important matter, so he gets up and joins her near the door. They converse quietly, while* KYLE *sits with his back to them, more interested in the plate of biscuits than what they are saying.*]

TRAVIS What does she want to see me about? Has there been some trouble?

MRS TURNER Well it's quite embarrassing really. Jill's been off school. Her dad's just died and when she came back this morning Mr Brewster shouted at her and said she'd been making a meal of it and that she'd been away too long. [*Pause*] Well, obviously she was ever so upset and she ran home.

TRAVIS [*Pause*] How long was she absent?

MRS TURNER Four days.

TRAVIS Mm. It doesn't seem excessive in the circumstances I must say.

MRS TURNER The trouble is, when Mrs Clifford phoned Mr Brewster to tell him that Jill'd be absent, he misheard and thought she said her *dog* had died.

TRAVIS Good lord!

MRS TURNER Anyway, she's waiting in the office if you'd like to see her.

TRAVIS Yes. I'll come down immediately. [*Then to* KYLE] You wait here. It'll give you the chance to think things over. Perhaps when I get back you'll have something to tell me.

[*He leaves the room with* MRS TURNER. KYLE *waits for a few seconds then stands up and takes a chocolate biscuit from the plate. He eats it hungrily, then takes another which he eats just as quickly. He rearranges the remaining biscuits then walks round the desk and sits down in* TRAVIS'S *chair. He glances at the contents on the desk then begins to swing from side to side on the swivel chair. He pushes hard, lifts his feet and does a full turn. Grinning, he repeats the performance. He then stands up and picks up the cricket team photograph which* TRAVIS *had looked at earlier. While he is studying it, he hears* TRAVIS'S *voice outside the room.*]

TRAVIS [*Voice over*] And don't think you've heard the last of this, Morris! I shall notify your parents immediately!

[KYLE *spits viciously on the photograph, runs back round the desk and sits down as* TRAVIS *enters the room brandishing a video-cassette.*]

TRAVIS Filth! Absolute filth! If we ran a shop selling video nasties instead of books, we'd make a fortune! There's obviously a thriving racket going on in school. [*He locks the cassette in a drawer in his desk*]

I'll catch them though, don't you worry. It's probably the same gang who broke in the other night. [*He sits down, places his hands on the arms of the chair and pushes himself out of his seat three times*] Do you know what they did Kyle?

KYLE No sir.

TRAVIS They broke into the media resources area and nailed a whole set of *Great Expectations* to the floor. [*Pause*] Can you imagine that! [*Pause*] Crucifying the classics! They should be horsewhipped!

Again, KYLE *has to fight hard to suppress his amusement.*

TRAVIS You don't know anything about it do you, Kyle?

KYLE [*Offended*] Do I heck! It's bad enough coming here in the day, never mind coming at night.

TRAVIS Yes. I can believe that. Judging by your attendance record, you probably wouldn't be able to find your way in the dark. [*He swings from side to side in his chair*] Why do you hate school so much Kyle? [KYLE *does not answer*] It's all you've got you know. It's your launching-pad to the future. [*Then, in an American accent, as if commentating on a rocket launch*] 5 – 4 – 3 – 2 – 1 – Zero! [*Pause*] We have lift off . . . [*He traces the path of the rocket with his hand until he is pointing at the ceiling*] The sky's the limit lad.

KYLE I don't want to be an astronaut.

TRAVIS [*Ignoring him*] That's where the future lies, technology. The sunrise industries. [*Pause*] The dawning of a golden age of leisure.

KYLE My dad's always saying he's a man of leisure since he lost his job.

TRAVIS Is that why you stole that money, to help out at home?

KYLE I didn't steal any money.

TRAVIS If that was the reason I can understand it. I don't condone it, but I can understand it.

KYLE [*Angrily*] Do you think my parents would take stolen money from me? They'd sooner starve first.

TRAVIS Look Kyle, this is getting us nowhere. I've wasted enough time with you as it is. This is a no-win situation as far as you're concerned so you might as well own up now. Look at the time! [*He jabs at his watch*] What are you going to do, sit here all through lunch break and afternoon?

KYLE [*Realising the implications of what* TRAVIS *has just said*] What about my dinner? Can't I go for that?

TRAVIS You're going nowhere until you've told me what you've done with that money.

KYLE You can't stop me.

TRAVIS Who can't. [*Then, menacingly*] Within the confines of this building I can do anything I want.

KYLE [*Pause, worried now*] But I'm starving. I only came for my dinner. I haven't had anything to eat since last night.

TRAVIS I don't care if you haven't had anything since last week! You're not leaving this office until I get to the bottom of this. Missing meals won't worry me. I'm on a diet anyway.

For the first time since he entered the room, KYLE *looks worried. He fidgets on his chair and looks towards the door.*

TRAVIS If you're thinking of making a bolt for it, forget it. I'll catch you before you leave that chair. One thing I've learned since I took up running is the importance of the start. If you don't make a good start you finish nowhere.

KYLE [*In mental torment*] And you promise you'll not tell the police?

TRAVIS I promise. Apart from Mr Shearer and myself, no one will ever know. Not even Weston.

KYLE [*After an agonising pause*] All right then! I did take it!

[*He looks as if he is going to break down and cry.* TRAVIS *sits back in his chair, triumphant.*]

TRAVIS At last. [*Pause*] Where is it?

KYLE [*Pause*] Behind the pipes in the boiler-house.

TRAVIS But why did you take it? It was so obvious. You must have known you'd be caught.

[KYLE *does not reply.*]

TRAVIS You must have been desperate, that's all I can say. [*Pause*] Are you in debt or something? Is somebody threatening you?

[KYLE *shakes his head.*]

TRAVIS Whatever it was, it must have been serious.

KYLE [*Pause*] I wanted to go to Fun City this afternoon.

TRAVIS [*Mystified*] Fun City? Where's that?
KYLE It's an amusement arcade in town.
TRAVIS [*Pause, then furious*] You mean you stole it to spend on slot-machines?
KYLE [*Shaking his head vigorously*] No, I only play *Attack*.
TRAVIS *Attack*? What's that?
KYLE [*Animated for the first time*] It's a video game about nuclear war. You score points every time you destroy one of the enemies' missiles. [*Pause*] I got in the *Hall of Fame* last week.
TRAVIS What do you mean?
KYLE There are two charts printed on the screen at the beginning of each game: *Today's Greats* and *All Time Greats*. If you score high enough, your total goes into the charts. I've been in *Today's Greats* a few times but never in the *All Time Greats*. That's my ambition, to get on that list. Him who's at the top goes in every day. Once he gets on, you might as well go home. [*Pause*] He's a genius . . .
TRAVIS [*Cutting him short*] Yes, I'm sure he is. I think you'd better go and fetch that money, lad. We've wasted enough time on this business already.

KYLE *hesitates, then stands up and leaves the room. As soon as he has closed the door,* TRAVIS *punches the air triumphantly. He then consults a list of telephone numbers and dials a number.*

TRAVIS Hello. This is Mr Travis, headmaster of Wordsworth School. Could I speak to Detective Sergeant Joyce please? [*Pause*] Right. Could you ask him to give me a ring as soon as he gets in? Thank you. Goodbye. [*He replaces the phone, looks at his watch, then dials again*] Hello Nancy, it's Mr Travis. Will you pop down to the gym please and ask Mr Shearer to come and see me? He should have finished teaching by now . . . Thank you.

[*He replaces the telephone, picks up a sports bag and takes out his running kit. He begins to get changed. There is a knock on the door.*]

TRAVIS Come in!

[SHEARER *enters the room. He looks embarrassed at seeing the headmaster half-dressed.*]

TRAVIS Come in Mr Shearer. I'm just getting ready for my lunch-time session. Fancy a run?

SHEARER I can't I'm afraid. I've got basketball practice with the fourth year. [*He watches* TRAVIS *getting changed*] What happened to Kyle?

TRAVIS Good news. I got a result. I've sent him to fetch the money. [*Pause*] Do you know why he took it?

SHEARER No. Why?

TRAVIS To spend in an amusement arcade in town. Pathetic isn't it?

SHEARER [*Pause*] It figures I suppose. They're home from home for some kids.

TRAVIS Anyway, it's out of our hands now. I've phoned the police; they can deal with it.

SHEARER [*Pause, then appalled*] But we told him nothing would happen! I gave him my word!

[*There is a knock on the door.*]

TRAVIS Come in!

[KYLE *enters. He looks embarrassed when he sees* SHEARER.]

TRAVIS Come in Kyle. Have you got it?

[KYLE *hesitates then takes a five pound note out of his pocket and gives it to* TRAVIS. *He avoids* SHEARER'S *eyes.* TRAVIS *holds the note up to the light.*]

TRAVIS Just checking.

[*He laughs but neither* SHEARER *nor* KYLE *look amused.*]

TRAVIS [*To* KYLE] Right then, off you go and get your dinner.

[KYLE *glances at* SHEARER *as he passes him.* SHEARER *gives him a sickly smile.* KYLE *leaves the room.*]

TRAVIS That's that sorted out then.

SHEARER What do you think I'm going to say to him the next time I see him? He'll never trust me again.

TRAVIS With a bit of luck you won't have to.

SHEARER I wouldn't have brought him if I'd known you were going to do that.

TRAVIS You had no choice but to bring him to me. That's what I'm paid for, to carry the can. [*Pause*] Anyway, I can't see why you should feel sorry for him. What's he ever done for the school? He's been a menace since the day he arrived. We've done our best, but we don't have the staff or the resources to deal with the likes of Kyle. He's an expensive commodity in educational terms and I'm afraid we can't afford him.

SHEARER He might get sent to Collingwood Hall with his record you know.

TRAVIS I would imagine that most members of staff wouldn't care if he was sent to Siberia.

SHEARER He's not a bad lad really when you get to know him. Quite bright really.

TRAVIS Oh, he's intelligent enough I'll give you that. But whether it's of the human variety is a matter for conjecture.

SHEARER He can be quite amusing at times . . .

[TRAVIS *is now fully dressed in his running kit.*]

TRAVIS Oh, I don't doubt it. The school's full of jokers, that's the trouble. We've got clowns and comedians by the score. If there were GCSEs in funny business, we'd have the best academic record in the country. [*He picks up a pair of novelty spectacles attached to a clown's red nose from his desk and puts them on*] Some of them even bring their own props with them to rehearse in class! [*Still wearing the false nose and glasses, he begins to run on the spot*] Are you sure you don't fancy a run?

SHEARER [*Looking at his watch*] No, I'd better go and get my dinner or I'll be late.

TRAVIS Watch the calories Mr Shearer. Perhaps you could give Kyle your pudding if you see him. [*He notices* SHEARER'S *puzzled expression*] That's how I got him to own up. I threatened not to let him go for his dinner. You should have seen the look of panic on his face. He said he hadn't eaten anything since yesterday. He must have been starving!

[SHEARER *looks at him in disgust.* TRAVIS *bends down and places his elbows on the desk.*]

TRAVIS How about a spot of arm wrestling before you go? I've discovered that strong arms are essential for good rhythm when you're running.

[SHEARER *hesitates, then crouches down facing* TRAVIS, *who is still wearing the false nose and glasses. He places his elbow on the desk. They grasp hands.*]

TRAVIS Ready? [SHEARER *nods*] Right then, after three. 1 – 2 – 3 . . .

[*The contest begins.* TRAVIS *is soon under pressure. His face goes red; he clenches his teeth and his eyes protrude.* SHEARER *easily takes the strain, then, slowly and deliberately, he forces down* TRAVIS'S *hand and with a final hard push cracks his knuckles on the desk.* TRAVIS *winces with pain.* SHEARER *keeps hold of his hand and looks him straight in the eye.*]

SHEARER Best of three?

TRAVIS [*Gasping*] No, that's enough. I don't want to take too much out of myself before the run.

SHEARER *lets go of his hand and they straighten up.* TRAVIS *massages his arm and rubs his knuckles. He looks shaken by the result of the contest.*

TRAVIS You've got a good arm on you there, Mr Shearer. Deceptive I must say.

SHEARER I used to play a lot of water polo at college.

TRAVIS That explains it. It's renowned for its devious tactics that game. Skullduggery under the water, that sort of thing.

SHEARER I don't think it's worse than any other game. There are cheats at all games as far as I can see. [*He glances at his watch*] I'd better go or they'll be knocking the gym door down.

SHEARER *leaves the room.* TRAVIS *stands looking at the door for a few moments, then starts a series of loosening-up exercises, swinging his arms, touching his toes, etc. He then starts running on the spot, fully kitted up plus false nose and glasses.*

FREEDOM LOG

DAVID CAMPTON

Characters

LEYDA
BOOM
SNICK
GREER
DYM
MABE
GUARD
OTHER GUARDS AND SETTLERS

The action takes place on Planet DPH/760 in a clearing and on a mountainside.

I was once asked 'Do you think it would be possible for a group of people to live together without any laws? Or, contrarywise, do you think that, if there were no police, it would be necessary to invent them? I wrote this play to find out – and still ended with a question mark. To give everyone a fair chance I set the scene on a far-off planet where they could all make a completely fresh start. Being only human, I suppose it was inevitable that they should make a mess of the experiment. In spite of the sombre ending, though, there is a comedy in this play and, if an audience should want to laugh, do let them.

[*Clearing near the edge of an alien jungle.* LEYDA, *alone, speaks into a portable tape recorder.*]

LEYDA [*Recording*] Here begins the Log of Expedition Freedom. Surveyor Leyda reporting. 17.00 hours – 15/10/2017. Crew members of Starship Bounty 149 have just disembarked from the module which brought us down to Planet DPH/760. Found guilty of mutiny, we have been sentenced to be marooned on this newly-discovered world. As the maximum penalty for mutiny is death, we could consider ourselves as having been dealt with lightly. Fortunately this is an Earth-type planet, and I was a member of the survey party, so we start with some advantages. Though as the only humans in an alien environment, this may prove to be merely a delay in execution. The Guards escorting us are not sympathetic.

[*There is a burst of laughter from* GUARDS *as they enter with the rest of the group.*]

GUARD You asked for it. You've got it.
LEYDA Our freedom.
GUARD A right mess if you ask me. Lucky for you Old Starchpants has a sense of humour. Some Captains I've served under would have had you pushed out through the air-lock. That's the regulation answer to disobeying orders – leave you to float between the stars.
LEYDA Would you have helped to kill us that way?

GUARD If I was ordered to – yes. I always obey orders.
LEYDA Always?
GUARD Second nature to me. I like obeying orders. You know where you are when you're obeying orders. While you're obeying orders somebody else is carrying the can. There'll be nobody to give orders on this new planet. You're going to feel very sorry for yourselves.
BOOM Sorry? Spitting in the Captain's eye was the best thing I ever did. I'm only sorry the mutiny didn't come off. Starship routine goes on just as before. 'Please, sir – permission to breathe.' If you'd half the guts of a squashed worm, you'd have joined us.
GUARD Less of that, Boom.
BOOM Trooper Boom to you.
GUARD Trooper nothing. You're off the Starship now. You're less than nothing. That's what dropping out leaves you with – nothing.
BOOM I'd sooner have nothing here than be back on that Starship.
GUARD At least you ate regularly on the ship.
BOOM To numbers. Eat to numbers. Sleep to numbers. Stand up to numbers. Sit down to numbers. Nobody's going to give me orders again – ever.
SNICK That goes for the rest of us, too.
GUARD I bet you believe in fairies.
LEYDA They're right. Life on this new world will be hard. We shall have to do without the comforts of civilisation. But we'll also do without the disadvantages of civilisation. We shall have no laws.
GUARD You've got to have laws.
LEYDA Why?
GUARD Well, because . . . because . . . everybody has laws. Laws tell you what you can and can't do. Without laws you'll end up a bunch of criminals.

LEYDA No. That is something no one in our community can be. If there are no laws, no one can break them.

GUARD [*At a loss for an answer*] Prisoners under escort are not allowed to chat up guards. That's orders.

[*Everyone except* GUARDS *laughs.*]

GUARD You know where you lot'll end up, don't you?

LEYDA We are here. We are on a new world. We shall make a new beginning.

GUARD A new beginning? With what? Without food or equipment.

LEYDA We have our hands and we have our heads. We shall survive.

GUARD You hope. Come on, you lot. Back to the module.

[*Exit* GUARDS.]

LEYDA As long as we all pull together.

[*The party watches them go.*]

LEYDA We must learn.

[*The party breaks into a babble, some despairing, some protesting.* LEYDA *tries to speak to them, but the babble rises. Eventually* BOOM *tops it.*]

BOOM Quiet there. Less of it. Shut up!

[*The babble dies down.*]

BOOM That's better. If everybody talks at the same time, we shan't get anywhere. What this meeting needs is a Chair who'll tell people when to speak.

LEYDA No, Boom.

BOOM I didn't say *I* wanted to be Chair, only that somebody has got to be in charge.

LEYDA Nobody is in charge. There will be no Leaders, or Captains, or Chairs. We are all responsible human beings.

BOOM What about you, Leyda? You started the mutiny.

LEYDA I was merely the first to defy the Captain. Then the rest of you backed me up.

GREER We followed you, Leyda. That makes you a sort of Captain yourself.

BOOM Right, then. You organise the meeting, Leyda. You'd better be quick, though. It's getting dark.

LEYDA I won't tell anybody what to do. That was the situation we have just escaped from. We mutinied against authority. Very well, from now on each of us must make our own decisions. It's not going to be easy – to start with we'll find ourselves all talking at the same time. But we'll never learn how to live together as long as there is someone to tell us what to do.

BOOM But democratically elected . . .

LEYDA Not even democratically elected. Here the only rule is that there are no rules.

SNICK [*Bored*] Hurray!

BOOM This is an emergency. We've been dumped at the edge of a forest with night coming on.

LEYDA So?

BOOM How can an emergency be dealt with if nobody gives orders?

LEYDA Use commonsense. When you're cold and hungry do you need telling to make fires and to look for food?

DYM But where can we find food?

GREER Where's the fuel?

LEYDA There's no place like a forest for finding wood. And at the top of that tree – see those things that look like nuts? Let's find out just how like nuts they really are.

[*Distant roar is heard.*]

GREER What was that?

DYM Thunder?

MABE Or was it the module taking off?

BOOM Sounded more like an animal to me.

SNICK An animal?

BOOM We're going to need those fires.

[*With a burst of chattering – 'Look for wood', 'Make fires', etc. – the group scurries out.* BOOM *is left with* LEYDA.]

BOOM Nobody gave orders. Oh, no.

LEYDA I gave advice. There's a difference.

BOOM And tomorrow?

LEYDA I'll suggest – only suggest – that we build a shelter.
BOOM Huh!

[BOOM *follows the group.*]

[*Lights fade.*
Lights come up.
LEYDA *is alone.*]

LEYDA [*Recording*] Freedom Log. Leyda reports. 16–10–2017. 14.00 hours. The building of the shelter has gone on since daybreak. The walls are made of bamboo-like poles, tied together with vines. We shall experiment with ferns for a thatch. Boom has been very good, lifting and carrying – and advising.

[*Enter the group with materials for building a stockade.*]

BOOM Hold it a minute. Tie it while I push. We need more vine . . . You there. Hey – you!

[SNICK *enters shaking nut shells with stones inside, pleased with the sound he is making.*]

SNICK Me?
BOOM Yes, you doing nothing. Fetch a length of vine.
SNICK I'm very busy. Listen.

[*He rattles the shells.*]

BOOM What do you call that nonsense?
SNICK Small round stones inside a shell. Ingenious, isn't it? If the food party manages to catch anything, I'll use the skin to make a tom-tom, then we'll have the effective beginning of a percussion band.
BOOM Listen, Neversweat – everybody here is slogging their guts out. All except you. Now . . .
SNICK I don't believe in work.

[*Continues to rattle shells.*]

[LEYDA *hurries forward just in time to prevent* BOOM *from attacking* SNICK.]

BOOM You little . . .
LEYDA Don't break Snick's neck, Boom. It may come in useful later.
BOOM You heard . . .
LEYDA I heard.
BOOM Are we going to put up with that rattle-waving while we . . . ?
SNICK Freedom of choice, Boom. I don't happen to choose manual labour.
LEYDA Yes, Snick. But the others have freedom of choice, too.
SNICK You mean you'll let that brute break my neck?
LEYDA No, Snick. We'll leave you to do whatever you want to do.
SNICK Thank you.

[*Walks away rattling the shells.* BOOM *turns on everybody else who has stopped to listen.*]

BOOM Haven't you lot got anything to do, either?

[*Everybody else gets on with their job.*
Lights fade.
Lights up.
The stockade has been completed. It is now dark except for firelight. With the exception of SNICK, *who cannot be seen, everyone is sitting eating.*
LEYDA *sits slightly apart with the recorder.*]

LEYDA [*Recording*] Log. 22.00 hours. Shelter almost completed. Food party caught small animal like a deer. Roasted this on spit over fire. Everybody tired, but satisfied.

DYM Don't tell me what this is, but it tastes good.

BOOM Where's that little squirt, Snick?

GREER He didn't help with the supper or the building, so he can't share in either. He's outside the fence, pretending he doesn't care.

BOOM He will.

[*An animal roars in the distance.*]

BOOM Hear that? It came prowling round last night, but the fire kept it away. Tonight the fire's inside the stockade.

GREER But Snick's on the outside.

BOOM He asked for it.
SNICK [*Off*] Hey, there!
GREER I think he's changing his mind.
SNICK [*Off, calling*] Let me in.
BOOM [*Calling back*] You chose to stay out there.
SNICK [*Off*] Now I'm choosing to come in.
BOOM [*Calling*] We've chosen to keep the gate bolted.
SNICK [*Off*] Open up.
BOOM [*Calling*] Come back when you've earned your keep.

[*The roar sounds louder.*]

DYM Listen to that!
SNICK [*Off*] It's coming this way!
BOOM [*Calling*] Good. I hope it's hungry.
SNICK [*Off*] Open this gate.

[*Out of sight there is a rattling and a beating at the gate.*]

BOOM [*Calling*] Rattle away. You won't break that down in a hurry.
SNICK [*Off*] Leyda. Leyda. Make them open the gate. You're in charge.
LEYDA Nobody is in charge here.
MABE Everybody shares.
SNICK [*Off*] I want to share.
GREER You didn't share in the work.
SNICK [*Off*] I'll work. I promise. Help! It's breathing down my neck. I'll do whatever you tell me to do.
LEYDA Nobody tells anybody here. We do what needs to be done.

SNICK [*Off*] Then somebody open this gate.
LEYDA Shall we?
BOOM Why?
LEYDA I think he's learned a lesson.
SNICK [*Off*] Help! I'll chop wood. I'll collect nuts. Please! I'll keep the fire going. I'll hunt for berries.
LEYDA Well?
BOOM I'll agree if everybody else does.
SNICK [*Off*] Don't stand about arguing. Let me in and have a vote afterwards.

[*A roar sounds very close.*
SNICK *screams.*]

BOOM All right, then. I'll open the gate.

[*He goes off, and a piece of wood is dragged aside.*]

BOOM [*Off*] Get in.

[SNICK *rushes in panting as the wood is replaced.*]

SNICK Nobody told me I was going to be fed to wild animals. I thought you didn't believe in punishments.

[*Sits sulkily and picks up a piece of meat.*]

LEYDA We have no laws and no punishments, but everybody has to face up to the consequences of their actions.

BOOM [*Returning*] See? If you'd been torn up, it would have been your own fault.

LEYDA Now you're inside you can sit by the fire. If you'll help to make spears for tomorrow's hunt, you can even have some supper.

SNICK [*Mouth full*] Thank you. All right.

BOOM Mouth full of meat already! Where did you pick that up from? Why, it was mine! The little devil's stolen my supper!

[*Everybody laughs.*]

BOOM You picked it up while I was bolting the gate. I knew we should have left you outside. Well, what are you lot going to do about it?

[*Laughter swamps* BOOM'S *cries of outrage.*]

[*Lights fade.*
Lights up on LEYDA *alone with recorder.*]

LEYDA [*Recording*] Log. 10.00 hours. 24/11/17. The community is settling down. Our building has been completed. That is now the meeting place. Other small huts are being erected.

[*The group enters, busy with various activities.*
SNICK *is chewing at a piece of honeycomb.*]

LEYDA [*Recording*] Everybody helps – even Snick from time to time. Of course there are minor irritations, and Snick seems to be behind most of them; but everybody seems to be getting used to living without rules. Except Boom. Odd that the one who most resented the Starship discipline should now be demanding laws.

[BOOM *strides angrily up to* LEYDA.]

BOOM We've got to come to some arrangement about food. Look at Snick, chewing away on that honeycomb.

SNICK If I risk getting stung, I ought to enjoy the honey.

BOOM We share food here.

SNICK Don't let me stop you.

BOOM Leyda, we must make rules. If we don't that little toad is going to make himself sick on any goodies he finds, and then try to share in the stuff we've pooled.

LEYDA You don't have to share with him, Boom. If he won't part with his honey, you just hold back your bread and meat.

BOOM We've tried; but he just steals what he wants.

SNICK You shouldn't leave food lying about. If you will lead me into temptation, what can you expect?

BOOM [*Enraged*] You . . .

SNICK [*Retreating*] Ah, ah, ah. If you try to do me an injury, I've a right to protect myself.

BOOM We need protecting against you. Leyda, surely you see by now that we can't live without any laws at all. A few simple ones will do – 'Thou shalt not steal' and so on.

LEYDA No.

BOOM Sneaks like him should be forced to work regularly and be punished for theft.

LEYDA Make just one law, and we'll have started a legal system. What's more, laws are useless without a police force to back them up. Who'll be our first policeman? You, Boom?

BOOM In the interest of law and order – yes.

LEYDA All the Starship regulations were made in the interest of law and order. We rebelled against them.

BOOM Our rules don't have to be Starship rules. But people can't live together without any rules at all.

LEYDA We are trying.

BOOM So that little pest is allowed to do exactly as he pleases.

LEYDA I didn't say that. If you have a quarrel with Snick, you must settle it between yourselves.

[DYM *enters waving to* BOOM.]

DYM Hi, Boom.

SNICK Oh, oh.

DYM Hey, Boom. Did you like the honeycomb I sent?

BOOM Honeycomb? What honeycomb?

[SNICK *tiptoes out with exaggerated caution.*]

DYM I asked Snick to bring it to you.

BOOM [*Furious*] I'll crush the little beetle! Where is he? Wait 'til I get my hands on him.

[*He rushes out after* SNICK.
All the others except LEYDA *follow as lights dim.*
Lights up on LEYDA *alone with recorder.*]

LEYDA [*Recording*] Leyda recording. 18.00 hours. 7/1/2018. Just returned to village after surveying expedition to the mountains. Caves up there that might be lived in. Find everyone has gathered around Boom and Snick. A sort of trial seems to be in progress. Won't they ever learn? For weeks I've kept their thoughts away from laws, but as soon as my back is turned – a trial!

[*Everyone enters in a tight group, arguing furiously.*]

LEYDA Stop that! Stop it!

[*The hubbub dies down.*]

LEYDA What is going on here?

[*The group parts to reveal* BOOM *and* SNICK. BOOM *is supported by an improvised crutch.* SNICK *keeps at a safe distance, but is prevented from running away by the rest of the group.*]

BOOM [*In pain and speaking with difficulty*] What are we going to do now, eh? Petty theft is one thing – attempted murder is something else.
GREER It's true. You should see Boom's wound.
BOOM The little devil tried to skewer me with a spear.
DYM Luckily it only caught Boom's side.
BOOM [*Roaring*] Lucky? . . . Ouch! [*Recovering*] A hole you could put your hand in? He tried to kill me.
LEYDA I'd like to hear Snick's version.

BOOM Of course you'll side with him.

LEYDA I'm not siding with anybody. I'm trying to find out what happened.

DYM I saw it all. Boom was chasing Snick, but I didn't take much notice of that, because it's always happening. Only this time Snick darted into the meeting hut where we keep the spears. Boom went in after him. There was a scream, and Boom staggered out with blood spouting. We found Snick crouching in a corner of the hut, still clutching the spear.

LEYDA Well, Snick?

SNICK It's true. I tried to kill him. He's been beating me regularly.

BOOM [*Raising a fist*] You deserved every . . . [*Clutches at the wound*] Ouch!

SNICK Last week he blackened my eyes, and yesterday he broke a tooth.

BOOM My mistake. I meant to break your jaw.

SNICK My mistake, too. I aimed at your belly, but I'm not very good with a spear.

BOOM You all heard that.

[*Murmurs from the crowd.*]

SNICK I was tired of being beaten. I had to stop him.

BOOM If the law had taken care of him, I needn't have had to beat him.

SNICK Wouldn't you? You're a natural bully. If we did have laws, you'd call yourself a policeman, and do it in the name of the law.

BOOM Just you wait until I can stand upright again.

GREER We really do need a few laws. We can't have people killing each other.

LEYDA Have laws ever stopped people from killing each other? Either you believe killing to be wrong and don't do it, or you do it – law or no law.
BOOM Of course if you're in charge . . .
LEYDA I am not in charge. No one is in charge. We are all free and equal.
BOOM Free to cut each other's throats without fear of being punished? It's time we had a few laws round here.

[*Cries of assent from the crowd.*]

LEYDA Do you all believe that?

[*Louder cries of assent.*]

LEYDA All of you?
SNICK Not me, obviously. I was born backwards, and that's the part of me I've shown to authority ever since.
LEYDA Do the rest of you believe this experiment has been a waste of time?
DYM Oh, no.
SNICK That makes three of us.
BOOM Three out of all this lot. There are going to be laws here whether you like them or not, Leyda.
LEYDA If you insist.
BOOM We do.
LEYDA But I shall not stay here. Laws are crutches.
BOOM Then we'll use crutches.
LEYDA Sooner or later other settlers will land here.
BOOM So what?

LEYDA They must find a community run the way we want it to be run – not based on laws or police, but on mutual respect and understanding.

BOOM We've tried that. It failed.

LEYDA I shall go on trying. I won't force my ideas on to anyone. I shall be moving on. But if anyone feels as I do, I'll be glad of their company.

[LEYDA *goes out.*]

SNICK Wait for me.

[*Hurries after* LEYDA.]

BOOM You're welcome to him.

[*Laughing the rest of the group follows.*
Fade lights.]

[*Mountainside near a cave.*
Lights up on LEYDA *with recorder.*]

LEYDA [*Recording*] Log of Expedition Freedom. Leyda recording. 18.00 hours. 10/7/2018. We have lived for six months in these caves – Snick, Dym, Cove and myself. In my darker moments I wonder what good we may be doing. Then I think of the others who must come in ten, twenty – a hundred years' time. They must find a community based on complete freedom. . .

[SNICK *enters making noises on a home-made pipe.*]

LEYDA Snick has made a sort of pipe, which is maddening because he should be collecting nuts and berries.

[SNICK *stops playing.*]

LEYDA Have you broken it? Thank goodness for that. Now perhaps you'll . . .
SNICK [*Pointing*] Look. Visitors.
LEYDA Visitors? Who . . . ?

[*Enter* MABE *and* WYE. SNICK *crosses to them.*]

SNICK Mabe, isn't it?
MABE That's right. And Wye. Wye doesn't say much since . . .
SNICK All the way from Boomtown. Well, what do you want?
LEYDA You'll have to forgive Snick. He never learned politeness. Sit down. Would you like a drink? It's only water, but it's cool and clear. There's a spring further along the path. How is everyone down in the village? We haven't seen anyone since we left.
MABE One of Boom's first laws forbad anyone to get in touch with you. I think he's afraid of you. We took a risk, but we want to join you.
LEYDA You want to . . . ?

MABE Boom is a very good organiser. Down there we have reveille and curfew, and organised guard duties. There's also a police station, and outside it are stocks, and a whipping-post and gallows.

LEYDA Gallows?

MABE Unused as yet, but there's a first time for everything. Boom says laws are no use unless everyone is sure about the punishments.

LEYDA Boom wouldn't . . .

MABE I think he would. You wouldn't survive for long down there now, Leyda. The stocks are used regularly. Anyone can be whipped even for saying that you were right. That's why Wye doesn't say much at all now. If Boom had caught us running to you, he'd surely have hanged us as an example.

LEYDA But you came to us all the same. Our ideas are taking root. They're spreading . . . [*Shouting*] Hey, Cove. Dym. Look who's here.

SNICK I'll take you to them. Do you like my pipe?

MABE *and* WYE *go out with* SNICK.
Fade lights.
Fade up lights.
LEYDA *is alone with the recorder.*

LEYDA [*Recording*] Log of Expedition Freedom. 9.00 hours. 8/12/2018. During the night Harb joined us. He is the fifth to come over, making nine of us here. I have proof that it is possible to establish a community without laws. With Boom for an alternative I am sure even more of the others will follow.

SNICK *runs in shouting.*

SNICK Leyda! Leyda! Look! Coming up the path. They're nearly here. A party with bows and arrows. And they're led by Boom.

[*The rest of* LEYDA'S *group enter behind* SNICK.]

LEYDA Boom himself! This is a triumph.
BOOM [*Off, calling*] Leyda, come out.
LEYDA I am out.

[BOOM *enters at the head of an armed group.*]

BOOM We marched up here unchallenged. Your guards are careless.
LEYDA Guards? Why should we have guards? We've nothing to be afraid of.
BOOM Syke and Hun keep your bows at the ready. We're not risking a surprise.
LEYDA We don't use weapons here. Why should we? We're all friends.
BOOM Leyda, you are coming back with us.
LEYDA You too, Boom? Have you come round to our way of thinking?
BOOM You're a disturbing influence. You and your outlaw gang. We're losing too many of our people. Last night Harb defected. We were ready and followed him. But there'll be no more taking the mountain path, because it won't lead to you any longer.
LEYDA Break up our community? Why? We're not harming you.

BOOM People object to obeying laws when they see others doing without them. You and your group are going to conform, or else.
LEYDA The stocks? The whipping-post? The gallows?
BOOM We're taking you back under escort. All of you.
SNICK Not me. You'll have to catch me first. Want to chase me up the mountain?

[*Runs off.*]

BOOM Shoot him.

[*Two of* BOOM'S *party run off. There is a distant cry as* SNICK *falls.*
The two return.]

LEYDA You killed him.
BOOM Saved us the trouble of hanging him. Come on.
LEYDA Give me a moment. I must finish something.
BOOM Just two minutes. The rest of you, this way.

[*The rest of* LEYDA'S *group are pushed off by* BOOM'S *followers.*]

BOOM Two minutes.

[*He goes off after the rest.*
LEYDA *takes out recorder.*]

LEYDA [*Recording*] Last entry in the log of Expedition Freedom. I shall not risk taking this recorder back with me. It could so easily be destroyed. I shall bury it under stones at the back of the cave. In a few years' time other settlers may land on this planet. I hope they will find, and listen and learn. Here is proof that people can live together without laws – if The Law will allow them. You, listening some time in the future, remember what happened here. For the time being – that is all.

[*Fade lights.*]

THE M & M CAFE

ANNE AYLOR

For my parents, with love

Characters

MONA MCCALLUM	A bottle blonde, early forties, widow of the Korean War. A hairdresser at Darlene's Hair Illusions, Ozona, Texas.
MARSHALL WADE	Rancher, mid-fifties, deeply tanned overweight. Owner of the Valverde Ranch, thirty miles outside Ozona.
CATO MCCALLUM	MONA's daughter, fifteen, high-school sophomore. Intense, pretty. She never smiles.
DOLORES BACA	Mid-sixties. Mexican cook and waitress. Owner of the M & M Café.
PANCHO	A dog.

The idea for *The M & M Café* came from a visit with my parents to a café in Aztec, New Mexico, several years ago.

When the waitress came to take our order, she asked us to look at her when we spoke because, although she was deaf, she could read lips.

Although this real waitress was replaced by a fictional DOLORES, what does remain of her in the play is her silent world and the inability of us all to communicate. Of people struggling to understand each other, of the difficulties of accepting change. Of the loneliness of loving and of feeling unloved.

The *santo* is an indigenous folk-art form of the American Southwest. These crude figures originated because of the scarcity of religious images in isolated settlements and were made by self-taught craftsmen out of aspen, pine or cotton wood.

The statues are prayed to in times of need; if the *santo* does not intercede successfully with God on the supplicant's behalf, it is temporarily turned towards the wall.

1957. A Mexican café in the middle of nowhere. Painted in reverse on the plate-glass window, THE M & M CAFÉ. A religious calendar and sombrero hang on the wall. A juke-box. A beaded curtain. Battered tables with glasses on them. In a niche above one table, a *santo*, a primitive religious statue carved out of wood. St Francis has his arms outstretched; on each sleeve perches a bird. Outside the window an arid landscape with clumps of yellow plants.

[*Early evening, the end of summer. Country and western music.* MONA *and* MARSHALL *enter. He carries an opened bottle of champagne; she a cone of yellow flowers.* MONA *points at the lettering* 'M & M' *with her bouquet as the music fades.*]

MONA You devil!
MARSHALL What're you talkin' about?
MONA You had that painted special.
MARSHALL [*Turning around*] I had what painted special?
MONA The Mona and Marshall Café.
MARSHALL More like Mexican and 'Merican.

[*He swigs some champagne.*]

MONA *[Teasing him]* You coulda pretended.
MARSHALL I had the sign painter in this mornin'.
MONA Marshall Wade, you're a lyin' devil.
MARSHALL You know I am. Come here.

[*He kisses her. Unseen,* CATO *stands outside the screen door watching in silent fury. They sit at a table downstage.* MARSHALL *fills two glasses. He hands* MONA *her champagne. He lifts his glass to toast her.*]

To my hunnert pounds a happiness.

[MONA *shakes her head.*]

I thought you weighed a hunnert pounds.
MONA Let's do it like they do in the movies.
MARSHALL How's that?
MONA You hook your arm around mine and drink from your own glass.

MARSHALL I ain't never seen nothin' like that. I'm jus' a hick rancher.

MONA Then jus' let me show ya.

[*She teaches him how. They toast.*]

MARSHALL Two weeks till we git hitched, Mona.

MONA Two weeks ain't long. Sure you don't wanna wait a bit?

MARSHALL When a man gits as old as I am, he knows what he wants. He don't fool aroun' makin' his mind up.

[MONA *plays with her engagement ring.*]

MONA Cato's takin' the news real hard.

MARSHALL She'll git over it.

MONA You think so?

MARSHALL Some people would gripe if you hung 'em with a silk rope.

MONA I didn't want her to find out all of a sudden.

MARSHALL How's I to know she'd figure it out?

MONA You shouldn't have tol' her it was a cocktail dress. One thing Cato ain't is stupid. [*Pause*] The crazy thing was, I was gonna tell her tonight after we got back to Ozona.

MARSHALL [*Looking around*] Where is she anyhow?

MONA In the pick-up.

MARSHALL Git her to come out. I'll try and make it up to her. You'll see.

[*He winks at* MONA. CATO *ducks out of sight as her mother goes to the door.*]

MONA Don't sit out there, hon. Come inside and help us celebrate.

[*She waits, then returns to the table.*]

[*Whispered*] She's comin'.

[MARSHALL *turns over a third glass and fills it with champagne.* CATO enters.]

MARSHALL You're in for a treat, Cato. The M & M has the best Tex-Mex food for a hunnert miles aroun'.

CATO [*Flopping into a chair*] Looks like a greasy spoon to me.

MONA Cath'rine McCallum! [*To* MARSHALL] I'm sorry.

CATO What're you apologizin' to him for?

MONA You mind your tongue.

MARSHALL You can't always tell a book by its cover, Cato. Cheers.

[*He pushes* CATO *her glass.*]

CATO You drunk from that bottle.

[*She pushes the glass back.*]

MARSHALL [*Sliding it to her*] What's a little spit between friends?

CATO [*Returning it*] You can keep your spit to yourself.

MONA [*Under her breath*] Just this once, behave yourself.

[CATO *pretends to read the menu as* MARSHALL *drinks champagne. Unseen,* DOLORES *watches through the beaded curtain.*]

The chimichanga looks real tasty.
MARSHALL It is. Ever'thing's good here.

[*He burps.* CATO *looks at him in disgust.*]

[*Hitting his chest*] Excuse me. Long time since I had a reason to drink that fizzy stuff.

[*He points at* CATO's *menu.*]

Know why they call it the Billy the Kid Special? The portions are so big they should be outlawed. Git it?

[CATO *ignores him.* DOLORES *leaves.*]

What are you havin' honey?
MONA I think I'll have the cheese enchiladas. [*Pause*] What're you havin'?
MARSHALL The No 2 with a side order of beans. What's your mouth set for, Cato?
CATO I ain't hungry.

MONA You ain't eaten nothin' since lunch.
CATO [*With great bitterness*] I feel sick to my stummack.

[MONA *and* MARSHALL *exchange looks.*]

MARSHALL Speakin' of stummacks, mine's startin' to grumble a bit. Dolores. Dolores!
DOLORES [*Off*] Si, Señor Marshall.
MARSHALL Git yourself out here. I want you to meet my fam'ly-to-be.

[CATO *starts to shred a paper napkin into confetti-sized pieces.*]

DOLORES [*Off*] I'll be there in a minute.

[*Kitchen noises, off.*]

MARSHALL I heard some new Aggie jokes.
CATO I don't wanna hear no Aggie jokes.
MARSHALL You used to like my Aggie jokes.

[CATO *rips up another napkin.*]

Would you like to hear some jokes, Mona?
MONA I'd love to.

MARSHALL Didja hear the one about the Aggie who froze to death at the drive-in?
MONA Naw.
MARSHALL He went to see *Closed for the Winter*.

[MONA *laughs;* CATO *groans.*]

Gimme another chance, kid.
CATO Why should I?

[MONA *pinches her daughter's leg.*]

Ow!
MONA Then behave yourself.

[MONA *adjusts her beehive.*]

MARSHALL This Aggie was drivin' down the highway doin' seventy miles an hour. He looks in his rear-view mirror and he sees this three-legged chicken tailin' him.
MONA A three-legged chicken?
MARSHALL That's right. Before he knows it, this ol' bird overtakes him and he jus' can't believe his eyes.
CATO *[Behind her menu]* He ain't the only one.
MARSHALL The Aggie floors it and passes the chicken at ninety miles an hour and don't you know, the chicken passes him doin' a hunnert and ten. All of a sudden the bird turns off the highway and the Aggie follows it into this farmyard. There's an ol' farmer

sittin' by the gate and the Aggie goes up to him and says, 'Did you see a three-legged chicken run in here?' 'Yep,' the farmer says. 'That's the fastest chicken I've seen.' The farmer says, 'It's one a mine. I breed 'em.' The Aggie says, 'Why'd you breed 'em with three legs?' 'Well,' the farmer says, 'I likes a leg, my wife likes a leg and my son likes a leg.' 'Whud they taste like?' 'I don't know,' the farmer says, 'we ain't never been able to catch one.'

[MONA *and* MARSHALL *laugh.*]

CATO That ain't funny. That's stupid.
MONA [*Teasing*] I thought you wasn't gonna listen to Marshall's jokes.
CATO I couldn't help it, could I?

[MARSHALL *digs in his pockets.*]

MARSHALL [*To* MONA] You got any quarters?
MONA What for?
MARSHALL I wanna see if they got Cato's favourite platter.

[MONA *finds some quarters and gives them to* MARSHALL. *He goes to the juke-box.*]

CATO Would you tell him to quit callin' me Cato.
MONA That's your name, ain't it?
CATO That's the name daddy give me. I'm Cath'rine to him.

MONA [*Pleading*] Would you stop bein' so difficult.
CATO You tol' me he was a friend. A good friend.
MONA Well he is.
CATO [*Lifting her leg*] Pull the other one.
MONA Put your foot down and start behavin' like a lady.
CATO You lied to me!
MONA [*Ashamed*] Cato, ever'thing happened so fast.

[MARSHALL *comes back to the table as 'I'm All Shook Up' plays on the juke-box. They sit in silence for some time.*]

MARSHALL Dolores! Tear yourself away from that kitchen and git out here.

[DOLORES *appears from behind the curtain drying her hands. She wears a chili-green uniform. Her name is embroidered over her heart.*]

Mona, Dolores Baca. Dolores, Mona McCallum.

[MONA *and* DOLORES *shake hands.*]

DOLORES Pleased to meet chew.
MONA Honoured I'm sure.
MARSHALL Dolores has been feedin' me ever Friday night for as long as I kin remember.

[*He smiles proudly at* CATO.]

And last – but certainly not least – this is Cato.

[DOLORES *smiles and extends her hand.*]

CATO The name's Cath'rine.
DOLORES [*Shaking hands*] Pleased to meet you, señorita.
CATO Likewise I'm sure.

[*Pause.*]

MARSHALL Well, Dolores?
DOLORES Jew're right.
MARSHALL Didn't I tell ya?
CATO [*Suspicious*] Right about what?
MARSHALL That you're the prettiest little doggie in the whole a Crockett County.
CATO [*Wanting to believe, yet disbelieving*] Sure.
DOLORES Are jew folks ready to order?
MONA The cheese enchiladas and a root beer, thank yew.
MARSHALL I'll have the No 2 with a side order of beans and a pitcher of –
DOLORES Pearl Beer.
MARSHALL See how well she knows me?
DOLORES And jew, señorita?
CATO I ain't hungry.
MONA Tell Dolores what you're havin'.

CATO I said I ain't hungry.
MONA Order, missy, or you're grounded for a month.

[*Pause.*]

CATO Billy the Kid Special.
DOLORES And a Billy the Keed. It'll be ready in about ten minutes.

[DOLORES *exits as 'I'm All Shook Up' ends. 'The Yellow Rose of Texas' starts on the juke-box. It is* MONA'S *favourite song.*]

MONA Oh Marshall!
MARSHALL Come on.
MONA Come on what?
MARSHALL Let's dance.
MONA Marshall –
MARSHALL Ain't no one else here. [*Teasing*] You dance with the one who brung you or else you walk home by yourself.

[MARSHALL *leads* MONA *to the middle of the floor. She dances stiffly; she feels* CATO'S *eyes on her.*]

[Singing] 'She's the sweetest little rosebud,
That Texas ever knew,
Her eyes are bright as diamonds,
They sparkle like the dew,
You can talk about your Clementine,

Or sing of Rosalee,
But the Yellow Rose of Texas
Is the only girl for me!'

[CATO *runs out of the café.*]

MONA *[Running after her]* Cato!

[MARSHALL *kicks a table.*]

Don't be angry at her!
MARSHALL I ain't angry at her. *[Pause]* I'm angry at myself.

[MONA *looks puzzled.*]

For rushin' ever'thing. [*Pause*] How's I supposed to know she'd take it this hard? I thought she liked me.
MONA It don't mean it ain't hard for her to swalla.
MARSHALL [*Hurt*] I been good to her. I gone outta my way to be good to her.

[MONA *plays with her engagement ring.*]

MONA She remembers her daddy. [*Pause*] She remembers ever'thing. He was always doin' some kinda trick. Pullin' palm trees outta newspaper, makin' cards disappear. He was jus' magic to her.

[*Pause.*]

MARSHALL I'll do right by her, you'll see.
MONA I know you will. But try and unnerstand it's a lot for her to take on board right now.

[CATO *appears in the doorway wearing a brown silk dress over her blue jeans.*]

[Horrified] What're you doin'?
CATO I wanted to see what your weddin' dress felt like on my skin.

[CATO *walks across the floor slowly. She stands in front of* MONA.]

It feels like tears.
MONA Look, Cato. I'm sorry –

[CATO *starts to tear the dress.*]

Cato!

[MARSHALL *grabs* CATO'*s arms.*]

CATO Lemme go!
MARSHALL Are you gonna behave yourself?
CATO NO!
MARSHALL Then I'll jus' have to keep holt.

[CATO *continues to struggle like a wildcat, but she's no match for him.*]

CATO You promised me you'd never git married again! You promised, you promised!
MARSHALL Is that what you tol' her?
MONA Ain't that what ever' widow says?

[MARSHALL *lets* CATO *go. She is crying.*]

MARSHALL You have a little talk with your daughter. I think I'll take a drive.
MONA *[Trying to stop him]* Marshall –
MARSHALL You two need to git a few things settled. Right now.
MONA What about our food?

[*He exits.*]

How could you do this to me?
CATO You tol' me you'd never git married!
MONA That was seven years ago!
CATO You swore when daddy was kilt. Up and down on the Holy Bible.
MONA What else could I do?

[CATO *slides under the table.*]

Git up from there. You'll git my dress dirty!

CATO He's a dirty old man!
MONA I don't even know why I'm talkin' to you.
CATO He's got a beer gut, a gold tooth. He burps at the table –
MONA [*Facing* CATO] You can't wait for perfection in this world. You take what happiness you can and run.
CATO You deserve someone better'n him!
MONA You're too young to unnerstand!
CATO I am not!
MONA Then quit actin' like a baby. Git up off that floor and listen to me. Come on now. Git up.

[CATO *does, slowly.*]

[*Indicating a chair*] I want you to sit there and listen to me for a while.

[CATO *sits reluctantly.*]

You think you know what it's like bein' a widow woman? You think you know what loneliness is?
CATO He makes me sick.
MONA You know how hard it's been for me since your daddy died. [*Pause*] Washin' smelly hair, givin' permanents. Curlin' hair so long I thought my arms 'ud drop off –
CATO I didn't ask to be born!
MONA Neither did I. [*Pause*] Nobody does.
CATO You didn't have to hook the first catfish that swum along!

[*Pause.*]

MONA He ain't the first.

[CATO *is shocked.*]

It's true. I coulda married five times if I'd had half a mind to, but they wasn't the right men, Cato. For me or for you.

CATO Marshall ain't the right man neither!

[*Pause.*]

MONA Look. I ain't gettin' any younger. Marshall might be no oil paintin', but he's a good man. A kind man.

CATO Good for what?

MONA I know it hurts, me marryin' again, but so does sprainin' an ankle or gittin' a shot. The thing about hurt is that it goes away. It jus' takes a little time.

CATO You'll have your M & M Café and Cato won't have no one!

[MONA *looks puzzled.*]

There won't be no room for me. It'll be like that letterin': M & M. No room to squeeze Cato in.

MONA There's always room for love.

CATO You're lyin' again!

[DOLORES *is seen through the beaded curtain with a pitcher of beer.*]

MONA Do you think I loved your daddy less when you was born?

CATO Leave me alone!

MONA Do you think I loved him less when I had somebody else to love?

[CATO *is silent.*]

Well do you?

CATO [*Bitterly*] Yes.

MONA You cast your mind back and think about it. I'll leave you right here to think about it.

[MONA *picks up her roses and exits. She crosses in front of the window and waits outside for* MARSHALL. *After a pause* DOLORES *enters with the beer.*]

DOLORES [*Indicating the statue*] Jew know what that is?

[CATO *shakes her head.*]

A *santo*. We put great faith in the powers of the *santo*.

CATO [*Putting her chin on her arms*] Big deal.

DOLORES In times of need the *santo* is offered prayers.
CATO I don't need nothin'.
DOLORES No?
CATO Nope.
DOLORES Everybody needs somethee n. A new pair of shoes, false teeth. Maybe to get a good report card?
CATO I make straight A's. [*Pause*] Well, almost. Whad he ever do for you anyhow?
DOLORES He found Pancho.
CATO Who's Pancho?

[DOLORES *whistles.* PANCHO *enters.* CATO *pets the dog.*]

Whaddya do? I mean, when you lost him?
DOLORES I gave the *santo* a gift.
CATO A gift?
DOLORES Somethee n of value so St Frances would intercede with God on my behalf. [*Pause*] I ask heem to find Pancho and bring him back. The next morning Pancho was here wagging hees tail.
CATO What if you don't git what you ask for? You don't always git what you ask for.
DOLORES Then jew turn the *santo* towards the wall like a bad boy.

[CATO *stares at the statue a long time.*]

CATO I ain't got nothin' to give.
DOLORES It can be flowers.
CATO There ain't nothing out there 'cept yellow rocket.

DOLORES St Francis has a special liking for jellow rocket.

CATO Yellow rocket's a weed.

DOLORES To heem all flowers smell sweet.

[CATO *hesitates, then stands up.*]

CATO You don't think he'd be offended? Bein' offered a weed?

DOLORES [*Confidently*] Nebber.

[CATO *exits and re-enters with a handful of yellow rocket. Self-consciously she arranges them at the* santo's *feet.*]

CATO Now what I do?

DOLORES Jew pray.

[CATO *folds her hands.*]

CATO [*Suddenly*] What if you don't believe?

DOLORES In what?

CATO In miracles.

DOLORES Then close your eyes and pretend.

[DOLORES *exits.* CATO *attempts to pray. She lifts her head occasionally to see if* DOLORES *is watching. A car is heard outside.* MONA *is seen talking to* MARSHALL. CATO *lowers her head.* MARSHALL *appears in the doorway. He clears his throat.*]

MARSHALL Mona and me are goin' bowlin', Cato. [*Pause*] You wanna come with us?

[CATO *stares at him.*]

We'll be leavin' in a minute if you wanna come.

[MARSHALL *puts some money on the table and exits. A car door slams. After a while an engine is heard.* CATO *runs to the door.*]

CATO [*Turning around, hesitating*] Dolores.

[CATO *waits for her to appear as the engine is revved.*]

[*Urgent*] Dolores!

[CATO *decides she can't wait any longer and exits.* DOLORES *enters as the truck drives off. She puts the money in her apron pocket and wipes their table.* DOLORES *stares at the* santo, *then wipes his brow playfully.*]

DOLORES [*To the santo*] Hard work, eh?

[*Black-out.*]

BREAKING POINT

STEVE BARLOW

Characters

GEORGE	West Indian aged nineteen. Pupil in Karate school.
WES	White aged thirty-odd. Karate instructor.

A few years ago I went into a pub in Nottingham for a drink with a black friend. A man in the bar started, as soon as we came in, to abuse us both – my friend because he was black, and myself because I was a 'nigger lover'. What upset me most was that no one told him to shut up.

When I went to Africa, I found many white people who believed they were superior to black people. I also met many black people who thought they were superior to white people.

Back in Nottingham, two Karate experts came to the school where I was teaching to give a demonstration, and very impressive they were. One of them was black. He was asked why he started doing karate. He admitted it was because he wanted to know how to beat up people he didn't like, but insisted that he had given up that idea very quickly, and never got into fights now. 'If someone calls me "Sambo",' he said, 'I just walk away.'

That did it, and I went home and wrote *Breaking Point*. It took me a morning to write the play, but it took me ten years to develop the idea.

A Karate Club

GEORGE [*Entering*] Hi, Wes.
WES Hello George.
GEORGE Nobody else coming?
WES Doesn't look like it.
GEORGE It's the snow.
WES The snow's not that bad. Some of 'em use it as an excuse. Sooner watch the telly or go boozing then come here and work.
GEORGE Come on, Wes, there's not many like that.
WES You got here.
GEORGE You know me. Never miss a session, do I?
WES Yes, very conscientious.
GEORGE Got to be conscientious if you want to get on.
WES And you want to get on.
GEORGE 'Course I do. You said I could make the national team if I worked.
WES You could.
GEORGE Well then. You OK?
WES Me? Yeah, sure.
GEORGE You seem a bit narky tonight. Bit short-tempered.
WES Do I? Must be the weather.
GEORGE Yeah, well, when you have weather in this country, you really have weather. You don't know when to stop. That snow out there must be two feet thick. Enough to depress anybody. Do you like snow?
WES Only on Christmas cards. Suppose you never get snow in Barbados.
GEORGE Trinidad. I told you before. My family come from Trinidad.
WES Oh, yes, you said. Same thing, isn't it?

GEORGE [*Shortly*] No! [*Embarrassed, laughing*] Not the same thing at all.
WES No? Well, you'd know more about that than I would.
GEORGE Want to get started?
WES Wait a bit. See if anyone else turns up.
GEORGE That's not like you. Usually it's, 'Come on, get changed, we haven't got all night.'
WES Could be I'm a bit knackered tonight.
GEORGE You're getting old, Wes.
WES Is that so?
GEORGE Comparatively.
WES Don't bother putting a deposit on a wheelchair just yet, sunshine. I've got a few years of active life in front of me.
GEORGE Can't be easy, getting middle-aged.
WES Can't be easy being young. Got a job yet?
GEORGE [*Shortly*] No.
WES Not many jobs about.
GEORGE Not if you're black.
WES Like that, is it?
GEORGE Come on, you know the situation. So I apply for a job. So first thing they do is, they clock my address: 'Oh, that's where the blackies live, isn't it?' Straight in the bin it goes. So I go to the factory. I can't get through the gates. I can't even get to see the man who matters. Mate of mine, he had qualifications. He talks his way in, finally, and sees the man, you know . . .
WES Personnel manager?
GEORGE Yeah. He say, 'look, I got these qualifications, so if you give the job to a white guy who got no qualifications, I am going to report you to the Race Relations.' Know what they did? They told him he was overqualified. Overqualified! Us blacks are all

either overqualified or underqualified; there's no just-right-qualified if you're my colour. My brother, now, he did get a job. Lasted a week. They froze him out. Wouldn't talk to him. Wouldn't sit next to him in the canteen. In the end, he asked a foreman, very reasonable, what he'd done wrong. The foreman said they didn't want no effing niggers. He belted the foreman: so they gave him the sack. My brother, I mean.

WES Upsets you, that sort of thing, doesn't it?

GEORGE What d'you expect? Would you like it?

WES Not much, no. Belted the foreman, did he?

GEORGE Yeah. Bloodied his snoot for him.

WES Disgraceful.

GEORGE Yeah.

WES Losing his temper like that.

GEORGE What? I thought you meant the foreman.

WES Shouldn't go round hitting people.

GEORGE Suppose not.

WES Suppose not?

GEORGE Alright, you shouldn't.

WES Like that do last night. Hear about that?

GEORGE No. Don't think so. What do?

WES It's been on the local radio all day.

GEORGE Haven't been listening to local radio.

WES Funny, I'd've thought you'd've heard about it. It was outside the Lion. You go in there, don't you?

GEORGE Sometimes.

WES Thought you might've been there.

GEORGE Not last night.

WES Well, apparently this bloke was drunk. Shouting the odds. Yelling we ought to send all the wogs home, you know, chuck the coons out, all that. He gets out of the pub, and there's a fight. Someone smashed his throat in.

GEORGE Yeah?
WES Smashed right in. They got him an ambulance. Nearly died on the way to hospital, they said. Still in a critical condition. You didn't hear about that?
GEORGE No.
WES Shows what can happen when you lose your temper. That's GBH, that is. If he dies, it's murder.
GEORGE Do they think he'll die?
WES They just said 'critical'. Mind you, he must have been a bit of an expert, the feller who did him.
GEORGE You reckon?
WES Oh, yes. You've got to know how to get power into a strike to do that kind of damage. Good thing it was your brother belted that foreman and not you, isn't it?
GEORGE He wouldn't've done anything like that.
WES I mean, that's no reason to belt a bloke, is it? Just for calling you a nigger?
GEORGE Sounds a pretty good reason to me.
WES No, I mean – it's just a word, isn't it? I looked it up once, in the dictionary – you know how you look up rude words like fart, just to see if they've put them in? Know what 'nigger' means?
GEORGE If you were me, you'd know what it means without a dictionary.
WES No, the point I'm making is, what it means – all it really means – is black. From Latin – Niger – it said. French has the same word – negrè.
GEORGE Mine of information, aren't you?
WES It stuck in my mind, see. That's all it means. Black. You don't object to being called black, do you?
GEORGE It's what I am.
WES So why belt a guy for calling you black?

GEORGE Come off it, Wes. It's not what you say, it's how you say it. 'Come here, nigger! Hush yo' mouf, nigger! Tote that bale, nigger! Get back where you came from, nigger!' These guys, they tell me to get back to where I came from – I come from Wolverhampton, for God's sake.

WES So when you come down to it, your brother thumped this bloke because he didn't fancy his tone of voice. Bit excessive.

GEORGE Now you're twisting what I said.

[*Pause.*]

WES What's his name?

GEORGE The foreman?

WES Your brother.

GEORGE Edward. Eddie for short.

WES Funny, that.

GEORGE What?

WES How you lot all seem to have English names. Kings' names. George. Edward. I mean, look at me. Wes. That's more a West Indian name, really, isn't it? Wesley Brown. If you didn't know, you'd think I was black and you were white, wouldn't you?

GEORGE So why did your mother call you Wesley?

WES Oh, she was strict Methodist, see, so she called me after Charles Wesley. Or maybe John Wesley. Same difference.

GEORGE You a Methodist?

WES Not really. Not really anything. Bit of a puritan, though. A bit strict, a bit of a stickler. Aren't I?

GEORGE Suppose so.

WES There you are. So my name says something about me. What does your name say about you?

GEORGE Nothing much.

WES Oh, I think it does. See, your mum, she must've thought ahead. Thought, when he has to apply for jobs, if they think he's black, they won't see him. So I'll call him George. Then no one'll know.

GEORGE What are you getting at?

WES I mean, be a bit of a giveaway otherwise, wouldn't it? If she'd called you a proper darkie name. Like Rastus.

GEORGE Are you winding me up?

WES Or Masambula. Or Sambo.

GEORGE You watch it, Wes. What's up with you?

WES You make me sick, that's what. Coming in here with your sob stories. Poor little nigger boy.

GEORGE I won't take that!

WES Your lot, you give me a pain. You come over here, five minutes off the banana boat and you're signing on the dole, scrounging a living off the rest of us, and then you start moaning.

GEORGE Shut it!

WES There you are, all over the place, doing white men's jobs, putting us out of work – I can't go into hospital without being pawed about by coon doctors and coon nurses . . .

GEORGE Shut it, Wes!

WES And all the time, you're whining, going on about racism, so you go rioting and burn people's houses, and beat policemen to death – well, if you don't like it here, get back off home where you came from . Get back up your trees. Monkeys. Apes. Dirty stinking niggers!

[GEORGE *lashes out at* WES. WES *blocks the blow.*]

GEORGE God! [*Pause*] Still fast, aren't you?
WES Good job. So it was you.
GEORGE What?
WES Lay in wait for him, did you? Outside the Lion?
GEORGE I wasn't in the Lion last night. Ask anyone.
WES Oh, your mates will all swear blind you weren't there. But you were. You did him.
GEORGE Whoever did him, he asked for it. Didn't he?
WES You reckon.
GEORGE [*Defiant and still furious*] He won't go shouting his mouth off about sending the coons home again, will he?
WES He won't be shouting about anything. You smashed his larynx right in.
GEORGE He asked for it.
WES Like hell! You know what you did to him? You stop to think? He could have died. He nearly did. You chopped him right across the windpipe. He couldn't breathe. He was choking. Drowning. Drowning in his own blood.
GEORGE You expect me to take what he said? What do you know? Every day, the looks in the street, the shopkeepers watching you in case you pinch something, the police stopping you. 'Where are you going, sir? What have you got in the bag, sir? Is this your car, sir?' The way they say 'sir'. The old bag in the supermarket. The fascist barman in the pub. The Nazi on the factory gates – the way they look at you. The eyes. The eyes that say, 'Get out of here, nigger!' They look at you. And they look at you.
WES There are laws about race relations.
GEORGE Laws are for whites, not blacks. You can't take a man to court for looking.
WES You can't half-kill a man for talking, either.
GEORGE Never said I did.

WES That's right.
GEORGE What are you going to do?
WES About this thing you never did?
GEORGE Going to the police, are you? Going to be a good boy, Wes?
WES What would I tell them?
GEORGE I wouldn't if I were you.
WES Don't threaten me, son. You couldn't take me a minute ago. Now, you never will.
GEORGE What?
WES Go on. Get out.
GEORGE You chucking me out? Out of the club?
WES That's right.
GEORGE You can't do that.
WES Why not?
GEORGE You've no proof.
WES I don't need proof. I know
GEORGE You can't – not now. I've been coming here years . . .
WES Four years. Just over.
GEORGE Have I ever been in trouble before? Have I ever belted anyone before? I've taken stick for years, you know that. Even here. Some of the blokes – I've heard them, I've never raised my fist before, have I?
WES But you have now.
GEORGE OK, alright, I have. That what you want to hear? I was pretty drunk myself. He was shouting about coons, and pointing at me. His mates were laughing. I didn't want a fight. I went out. I waited for a bus. He came out. On his own. He started on at me again. He called me a mother . . . called me everything he could think of. I took it. I stood there and took it. Then he spat at me. Spat at my face. I could feel his spit running down. Something broke. I don't even remember hitting him. All of a sudden, he

was on the ground, twitching, making horrible noises, like gargling. Blood coming out of his mouth. The pub door was opening. Nobody had seen. I ran. I've seen his face all day. Heard that noise. I'll never forget it. All my life. Isn't that punishment enough?

WES No. Because it won't be all your life. You'll forget – you're already forgetting. Not what happened, but how you felt. You'll keep telling yourself he asked for it. Eventually, you'll come to believe it. Then somebody else will shoot his mouth off – like I did just now.

GEORGE I never hit you!

WES Wasn't for the want of trying, though, was it? And it'll get easier to lash out. It'll get easier every time.

GEORGE You're wrong. It'll never happen again – never. Look, this is my life. Karate. I had nothing when I started this – now I could be an international; be someone, someone who matters. I could do something for my brothers, get some respect. I could be world champion, I know I could.

WES No.

GEORGE I could!

WES All that might have happened before last night. Now it never will. You haven't the temperament. Even if I kept you on, you'd never make it. But I can't keep you on. And I'll make sure the word goes round: nobody else will take you on, either. It's all over, George.

GEORGE For one mistake?!

WES You can't afford one mistake. What I've taught you carries a responsibility, George. You've got to take all the stick anyone can hand out to you, *because* you don't have to, *because* you could stop them if you wanted. And you couldn't take it.

GEORGE But I didn't kill him, did I? Even as mad as I was, I pulled back. I could've killed him easily.

WES Then be thankful you've been stopped before you did kill someone. You're not safe.

GEORGE Neither are you, then.

WES Oh, yes, I'm safe. It's not ability, George. It's character. I could kill if I wanted to. But I've never wanted to. It's like cars. Cars aren't dangerous by themselves. What makes a car safe or dangerous is its driver.

GEORGE I took it, Wes. I took it for years. Don't I get any credit for that?

WES But something broke, didn't it?

GEORGE Every man has a breaking-point, Wes. What's yours?

WES I don't know. Nobody's found it yet.

GEORGE Then don't be so god-damn superior.

WES I'm not. I'm not you, George. I'm not a black man in a white man's country. Maybe I'd have broken sooner than you did – or later. Doesn't matter. You lost control. You can't ever do that, not in Karate. I'm sorry, George.

GEORGE Yeah. Me too.

WES What will you do?

GEORGE I thought of giving myself up. Then I thought – prison. If this is how blacks are treated outside, what must happen in there? I don't know. Maybe he won't remember what happened. He was drunk enough.

WES Maybe.

GEORGE I don't know. I'll have to think about it. Goodbye, Wes.

WES Goodbye, George. No hard feelings?

GEORGE About what?

WES What I said. All that – filth. But I had to know.

GEORGE That's OK.
WES Take care.
GEORGE That's a damn stupid thing to say.
WES Suppose so. But anyway.
GEORGE Yeah. [*He goes to the door; looks out*] It's still snowing.

[*He turns his collar up and goes out into the night.*]

PLAYWRIGHTS

Howard Barker

Howard Barker was born in 1946. The first performance of one of his plays, *Cheek*, was in 1970 at the Royal Court. As well as writing many plays for the stage, including *Edward, The Final Days, Claw,* and *No End of Blame*, he has written for radio and television.

Ken Whitmore

Ken Whitmore was born in Hanley, Staffordshire, and was a journalist for 20 years before turning to the writing of fiction. He has written more than thirty plays for radio and the stage, many short stories and a children's novel, *Jump!* (published by Oxford University Press). He was winner of the Times – Jonathan Cape children's story competition and of the Giles Cooper Award for radio drama. He is married with four children and lives in Cumbria.

Peter Terson

When I was doing a course in Writing for Sixth Formers with the Arden Foundation, a girl came up to me and asked, 'Are you Peter Terson?'

'Yes,' I replied.

She looked at me with wonder and said, 'I thought you must be dead.'

Well I'm not dead, but looking back my early life seems another existence.

I was born in 1932, the son of a joiner and last child of a mother worn out with 'work and worry'. The two 'W's of that period.

I was brought up on bread and dripping and passed the Entrance Exam for Heaton Grammar School, so much to my father's amazement that he told me to ring up the Education Office to see if they'd made a mistake.

However, I'd passed, but finishing with an undistinguished record have always feared my father may have been right.

I then had three consecutive failures, as a draughtsman, as an airman and as a teacher, then I sent a play to the Victoria Theatre, Stoke on Trent, and the Director, Peter Cheeseman, nominated me as Resident Playwright and the Arts Council gave me a year's salary of £900. While I was there Michael Croft of the National Youth Theatre asked me to write a play for 'about a hundred kids' and I wrote him *Zigger Zagger*.

They were my glorious days, but I'm not dead yet and just coming up to my peak. (Confidence and mad optimism are all to the playwright.)

Mary Cutler

Mary Cutler was born in Birmingham in 1949 and has lived there ever since apart from three years at University in Cambridge. She taught until 1979 when she became a full-time writer. She has written scripts for *The Archers* and *Crossroads*. Her stage play *Left In The Nursery* was produced in the Birmingham New Writing Festival. *Waiting For The Party* is her first published play. She has held several writing residencies for West Midlands Arts at Sidney Stringer School, Coventry, Selly Oak Library, Birmingham, and the Midlands Arts Centre, where she started a Young Women's Writing Group. She has reviewed and written articles for *Arts Report*, *New Socialist* and *The Guardian* and published fiction in *People to People* and *A View From Tindal Street*. She started her writing career contributing stories to *Jackie* when she was still at school. She has two daughters, Rebecca, sixteen and Helen, six.

Barry Hines

Barry Hines was born in Barnsley, Yorkshire, on 30 June 1939, and was educated at Ecclesfield Grammar School and Loughborough College of Education. He taught P.E. in secondary schools in London, Barnsley and South Yorkshire. He was Fellow in Creative Writing at the University of Sheffield, Matlock College of Further Education and University of Wollongong, New South Wales, and has written novels, short stories, plays and television plays.

David Campton

I started life in 1924 on top of a barber's shop in Leicester, and began to write shortly afterwards. In fact I have been writing for as long as I can remember. A little later I went to work for The Gas Board, leaving in 1956 to write for a living: no doubt to the relief of The Gas Board, which did not replace me (the job I was supposed to have been doing just vanished).

In the early years of The Scarborough Theatre in the Round I became closely involved with the running of a theatre as writer, actor, director and even theatre manager – which is a good way of learning how to become a playwright. Parts played while I was an actor included Noah, Pickwick, Polonius and a cottage loaf, which will give some indication of what I must look like.

As years have rolled by I have written for almost every medium. In addition to over a hundred stage plays (with forty years of writing, the scripts tend to pile up and some of the plays are very short) there have been radio and television scripts, short stories and books – even musicals for a Leicester Youth Group. I have never yet written a screenplay, because no one ever asked me to, but I suppose there is still time even for that.

Anne Aylor

Anne Aylor was born in New Mexico and has lived in England since 1973. She was a professional dancer and now teaches ballet at an adult education institute. *Children of the Dust*, her first play, won the 1987 South London Playwriting Festival and is to be produced in 1988 at the Soho Poly Theatre, London, and the Warehouse Theatre, Croydon. The one-act play in this anthology she hopes – if the Muses are willing – to develop into a full-length work.

Steve Barlow

Steve Barlow was born in Crewe and educated at Crewe Grammar School, and the Universities of Warwick and Nottingham before joining the teaching profession. After this he decided to find an honest job, and worked for several years in community theatre and Theatre in Education in Nottingham before moving to Norwich to join the DaSilva Puppets. Subsequently he taught English in a village school in Botswana for four years before returning to Nottingham. Steve Barlow is a lecturer at Clarendon College, Nottingham. He lives on the edge of Shipley Park in Derbyshire, and is often to be seen walking around it, muttering darkly.

ACTIVITIES

The Smile

by Howard Barker

If a play shows everyday events with believable characters speaking as they would in real life, we say it is **naturalistic.** Howard Barker has written a play which is **not** naturalistic. Compare *The Smile* with *Fun City*, *Breaking Point* or any other naturalistic plays you know. What differences are there between these plays and *The Smile*?

Brainstorming

There is no simple answer to the above question: you will find lots of differences. Some may help you to understand the play, some may not. A useful technique to help you explore this play is *brainstorming*. You'll need a blackboard or a markerboard or a large piece of paper and a pen. One member of the group is chosen to write down any comments the group may make. Anyone can make any comment they like about the play. It can be a phrase or a single word; it doesn't matter which. Do not argue or edit; just write down everything that is said, no matter how silly it may sound.

After a pre-set time limit, for example, 5–10 minutes, examine what you have and try to arrange the comments into some sort of order. Cut out any unhelpful comments and repetition. What is left can be discussed and expanded in order to help you understand the play.

Interpretation

Images are used by writers to create mood and atmosphere. For example, some romantic novels end with the hero and heroine gazing at, or walking off into, the sunset. The sunset, being the end of the day, is an image indicating the end of the story. Different types of images have different functions. A **symbol** is a simple image that stands for something more complicated. For example, a cross represents the Christian church, an inverted Y inside a circle represents the Campaign for Nuclear Disarmament. Badges are often symbols. If your school has prefects' or monitors' badges, they may be shaped like a shield. Why do you think this shape has been chosen? What does it suggest?

The central symbol of this play is the smile itself. What does the smile suggest to you as a reader? What does it suggest to the characters in the play? Use the brainstorming technique to explore this question.

Do not look for *correct* answers; Howard Barker is challenging you to use your own imagination, judgement and instincts. He himself may not have a completely clear picture of what he *means*! In *Waiting For Godot*, a play written by Samuel Beckett, two tramps are waiting for a mysterious character called Godot, who never appears. When asked who this character was, Beckett snapped: 'If I knew who Godot was, I would have said so in my play!' A play like the Smile invites *your* reactions and thoughts, which are just as valid as anybody else's.

What do the following suggest to you?
The Old Man: never shouting slogans
never hanging up flags
pretending to agree with people
not praying
not throwing roses

Does an overall picture begin to emerge?
What do the following symbolise?

dancing
the carnival
the sound of guns at the end of the play

Staging

The Smile is not a realistic or naturalistic play. This presents problems when it comes to staging or acting out the play. How, for instance, would you stage the Old Man's head coming off?! Suggest ways you might overcome this difficulty.

If you act out *The Smile*, it becomes obvious that a different *style* of acting is needed. For example, many of the characters ignore the presence of other characters and speak directly to the audience. The Old Man is killed very early on in the play, yet he continues to speak! This type of acting is called **stylised**. This means that it is not realistic but is representative. The actors are not trying to be *real* people but are representing a particular character. We should never forget that they are actors.

This type of Theatre is known as **Epic Theatre**. A German playwright called Bertolt Brecht developed this form of theatre in the mid-twentieth century. He believed that plays should involve the audience in thinking about what they are seeing. Consequently, his plays usually have a message for the audience to discover. He also believed that Drama should not create the illusion of reality and attempted to present his plays as a series of loosely-connected scenes, rather like a documentary. To link these scenes he used a variety of techniques including songs, projected messages and direct narration.

The narrator is very important in Epic Theatre. Who is the narrator in *The Smile*? Is there more than one narrator?

Do you think that there is a message in *The Smile*? If so, what is it? Is there more than one message?

To discover more about Bertolt Brecht and his theories on acting turn to the Further reading section.

Improvisation

To help you to explore the idea of stylised acting, try these following exercises:
Work in pairs. Choose characters and a location. Improvise a scene with those characters in the chosen location. However, you are not allowed to use normal dialogue, you can only use numbers! This exercise makes you concentrate on character and relationships rather than words.

In slightly larger groups improvise a scene in which which every every word word is is repeated repeated! This will help you to concentrate on what you are saying.

Each person in the group chooses a selection of foods, for example, cheese, pork pie, salad cream. Improvise a scene using only these words.

The object of these exercises is to focus attention on action, atmosphere and relationships, rather than on dialogue.

Character

In other plays in this Volume, we have looked at character. From what has been discussed, do you think it is important, or even helpful, to explore character in this play? If not, why not?

Project

Although you may not wish to explore the personalities of the characters, everyone will have an idea of what the characters look like.

If you can draw, draw or paint a picture of the Old Man or Old Woman.

Or: Go through some magazines and cut out pictures of people that correspond to your idea of what any of the characters look like.

Or: Take a camera into the streets and photograph people who have similarities to the characters in *The Smile*. Ask their permission first!

Or: Take on the role of the Old Man or Old Woman. Write down your impressions of your partner. In role, record your impressions on video or cassette.

When you have done this, pool and discuss your results. How much similarity or difference is there in the various pictures and tapes you have constructed?

Further reading

Bertolt Brecht wrote many plays, many of which are easily obtainable. The following are excellent examples of Epic Theatre: *The Caucasian Chalk Circle, The Threepenny Opera, Mother Courage, The Life of Galileo* and *The Resistable Rise of Arturo UI.*
Oh What a Lovely War is a popular play telling the story of World War I through songs, dance, newspaper headlines and photographs. It is a very enjoyable example of documentary theatre.

The Smile can be described as belonging to the body of work known as the Theatre of the Absurd. It is called this because impossible things happen. For example, in *Rhinoceros* by Eugene Ionesco, the chief character finds that all the people around him are turning into rhinos!

Other absurd writers include: Samuel Beckett (*Waiting for Godot, Endgame*), Jean Genet (*The Maids*), N F Simpson (*A Resounding Tinkle*), Harold Pinter (*The Caretaker*) and Edward Albee (*Who's Afraid of Virginia Woolf?*).

Battle in Budapest

by Ken Whitmore

This play, like *Slave!* in Volume 1, deals with a moment in history. However, *Battle in Budapest* deals with fictional rather than real characters, caught up in a real historical event. Joszef, Laszlo and Borbala are characters created by Ken Whitmore in order to explore the situation which has arisen about them. He is not concerned with the reason *why* there were Russian tanks in Budapest in 1956, but is interested in *how* they affected the people of the city.

Interpretation

Stage directions

The play opens with a long stage direction giving detailed instructions on the appearance of the set and characters. What does this contribute to our understanding?
Is it necessary?

Would it be a help or hindrance to a director of this play? In *The Smile*, another play in this Volume, there are very few stage directions, giving the director more freedom in their choice of set, costume or appearance of characters. Some authors provide us with numerous stage directions and explanatory notes (George Bernard Shaw or Tom Stoppard, for example), others (William Shakespeare for one) hardly use any. What are the advantages and disadvantages of these two methods? Which do you prefer?

Realism

In the opening stage direction, it is clearly indicated that the set should be as realistic as possible. The situation itself is real, in the sense that the invasion of Hungary actually happened.

But, how real is the dialogue? How does it compare with *The Pressure-Cooker* in Volume 1 of *New Plays* or with *Fun City* in this Volume?
Read the play again, deciding whether you think the dialogue is realistic or not. Support your view with examples from the script.

Humour
The play is about a tragic event, but it contains elements of humour. Identify these. Do you think they add to or detract from the serious issues of the play?

Extra scenes

A **tableau** is a group picture representing a moment in time. It is an attempt to make a living sculpture, painting, statue or photograph by using members of the group to capture a specific moment. It should capture the most vital elements of a situation.
Here are two ways you can go about building a tableau:
Stand in a circle. One person moves into the middle,

takes up a position and holds it (take care not to move). The other members of the group join in one by one to add to the picture created by the first person.

or:

Everybody, except one person, moves into a position and holds it. The remaining member of the group is the sculptor. The sculptor moves the others into positions which they think are more appropriate to the overall tableau. Take it in turns to be the sculptor.

Try both methods to see which produces the best results.

Tell the story of the Battle in Budapest in a series of tableaux: you could use the following headings:

News on the radio.
Building the barricades.
Fighting tanks with sticks.
The siege at Ranki Street.
Prisoners are rounded up.
The mothers of Budapest weep.

Spend some time on creating these pictures, taking care to make sure all gestures, looks and positions blend in to provide a complete picture.

When you have completed these, photograph them.

Improvisation

Here are suggestions for some extra scenes you can develop and explore in order to help your understanding of the play.

When Joszef and Borbala emerge from the building, what do they find?

If Laszlo survives, improvise a scene between him and Borbala.

If he dies, improvise a scene where Borbala tells her mother of his death.

Improvise the scene in which Laszlo meets the Russian patrol.

Improvise a scene in which Joszef tells his mother of the death of his father.
Improvise or script any other scenes you wish to explore.

Character

Use the hot seating technique described in the extension work to *Fun City* on page 165 in order to question Laszlo, Joszef and Borbala. Try to discover their thoughts on the invasion. How do these thoughts differ?

Which character in the play do you most admire?
Which character do you most sympathise with?
If you have given a different answer to each of these questions, why do you think you have done so?

Group discussion

Laszlo claims he would like to kill someone. He is twelve. What are your views on his statement?

Do you think it is right for children to be fighting? Can you think of any real situations, occurring in today's world, in which children are fighting soldiers?

Joszef is prepared to die for his beliefs. What would you be prepared to die for? If you are prepared to die for your country, you would be called a patriot. Would you die for your country?

Read Roger McGough's poem *Why Patriots Are a Bit Nuts in the Head*; you will find this in *The Mersey Sound* (Volume 10 of Penguin Modern Poets). Do you think this is a fair poem or is it just cynical?

Do you think either Joszef or Borbala wins their argument? Which side, if any, do you take?

What is suggested by the way the play ends?

Project

Find out the basic facts of the 1956 Hungarian uprising. Based on these and the events of the play, select one of the characters and write their diary covering the crucial period. If you feel your character would survive, you can take it further than the actual surrender. If not, end with the last entry that character would make.
or
Write a front page article describing the invasion for:

a a British newspaper
b a Russian newspaper
c a Hungarian resistance news-sheet

Further reading

There are many plays and novels about war. Perhaps the most famous war novel is Joseph Heller's *Catch* 22, a brilliant and funny book on the stupidity of war. *Oh What a Lovely War* explores World War I with song and dance. Bertolt Brecht's play, *Mother Courage*, examines the effect of war on individuals. R C Sherriff's *Journey's End* is one of the most famous war dramas. Shakespeare, especially in his history plays, has much to say on the nature of war.

Nuts

by Peter Terson

Nuts is a play about a family argument. It begins with the minor incident of the father forgetting to bring back some nuts for his son. This then develops into a full-blown argument, engaging every member of the family and ending up with the family deserting the father.

Exercise

Work in pairs. Begin an argument over something trivial, for example, cutting a loaf of bread crookedly or leaving the top off the toothpaste. Develop this argument, bringing in new accusations and points, until the original argument is forgotten.

Interpretation

At first sight, *Nuts* appears to be a comedy. However, it is a very sad play exploring the fragile relationship of the family. Consider the following points in order to help you explore and develop your understanding of the play:

Why do you suppose Peter Terson has Robbie asking for some nuts, instead of something more expensive?

What do we learn about Dad from Mum's warning to Robbie and Tracey that they may be disappointed with their presents?

Dad forgets the nuts and upsets Robbie. In what other ways does he upset his son? And Tracey? And Mum?

Dad saw the poncho and 'thought of Robbie like Clint Eastwood'. How does this help bring Robbie to the point of telling him what he thinks of him?

How is the isolation of Dad emphasised at the end of the play?

He says that his family has isolated him and the kids don't return his feelings. Is he right?

Character

The family begins slowly to split as Robbie, Tracey and Mum are drawn into the argument. At which points in the text do the different characters turn against the father?

Use the following moments and lines from the play to write a brief character sketch of Dad:
He twice suggests buying nuts from the supermarket and passing them off as coming from Spain. What does this tell us about him?

ROBBIE You want it all your own way don't you?

MUM I think you've tended to lord it over him with your own achievements.

TRACEY Buying love. You were always good at that.

DAD Complete loner in my own family.

DAD I don't need you lot!

Find some more lines which help your understanding of Dad's character.

Use the same technique of finding quotations and references, to use as a guide in writing brief descriptions of Robbie, Tracey and Mum.

Which character do you sympathise most with? Which character do you sympathise least with? Explain your reasons.

Hot seating

Use the hot seating technique described on page 165 to discover more about the characters and their feelings towards each other.

Hot seat Mum and ask her what she thinks of her

husband's behaviour. Why does she try to act as a mediator between Dad and the kids?

Hot seat Dad, Robbie and Tracey. Ask them what they think of each other.
Ask each character the following questions:
Do you think there is anything *you* can do to improve the way you all feel towards each other in your family?
Would you be prepared to make such a move?

Who is the most forgiving character and who is the most stubborn?

Extra scenes

You can explore and add to your understanding of a play by improvising extra scenes, based on the events of the play. Here are some suggestions for scenes you can improvise:
A scene in which the family meets next morning at the breakfast table. Do they come together again or have they drifted too far apart?

A scene in which Dad goes down to the pub and tells his friends how his family has treated him.

A scene in which Mum and Dad take their marital problems to a marriage guidance counsellor.

A scene in which Robbie or Tracey talks to a schoolteacher about the problems at home.

Role play

For an explanation of how to use the technique of role play, see the extension work to *Fun City* on page 167.

Tracey says to Robbie 'You're just trying to gain attention for yourself.' This role play explores the way people gain attention.

Choose two members of the group to host a party.

The rest of the class are guests at the party. Each person should attempt to become the centre of attention through their actions or what they say. How 'over-the-top' will people go in order to achieve this attention?
Start the role play as the guests begin to arrive.
NB There should be *no* physical contact!
After the role play has ended, discuss the results. Which attention-gaining methods were the most successful and which were the least?

What sort of things do you do in everyday life in order to gain attention?

Group discussion

Has any of your group ever had an argument which has blown up from a seemingly trivial incident to a full-scale confrontation?

Have you ever made a promise which you haven't kept, either on purpose or because you forgot? How binding to you are promises?

Have you ever been promised something which has then not been given?
How did you feel about this?

Further reading

Many plays deal with marital breakdown. Tom Stoppard's *The Real Thing* is a good example of this. Alan Ayckbourn's plays are often thought to be harmless fun, but there is a lot of cruelty in them. *The Norman Conquests* and *Bedroom Farce* are amongst his best plays. Arguably, the most moving and horrific picture of the end of a relationship is *Who's Afraid of Virginia Woolf?* by Edward Albee. Elizabeth Taylor and Richard Burton star in the film version of this play.

Waiting for the Party

by Mary Cutler

In her introduction to *Waiting for the Party*, Mary Cutler says that it is all about the relationship of the sexes. However, in the play, the boys and girls never actually meet! What do you think this tells us about the relationship between teenage boys and girls? Do you think it is a realistic play in the way it portrays this relationship?

Interpretation

A lot of the humour in this play comes from recognising that the characters are acting like we would in that particular situation. Many of you may associate yourself with a particular character, realising that you have said the same thing as them or behaved in an identical manner. This is called *Recognition Comedy*, and is probably the most popular form of recent comedy. We still have stand-up comedians, but instead of beginning 'Have you heard the one about . . .' or, 'There was this bloke . . .', they are more likely to start 'Have you noticed how . . .'. They don't tell jokes as such but talk about familiar things or day-to-day occurrences and invite us to laugh at some of the stupidity of our daily lives. Two popular comedians who work in this way are Victoria Wood and Billy Connelly. How many other comedians can you think of who work along similar lines?

The boys and girls in *Waiting For The Party* never meet. The script cuts from one group to another. What effect does this have on the play? Why does the play end where it does? How would you stage this play?

Scene 3 is odd. Usually, actors pretend to be talking to each other and to be unaware that they are being watched by an audience. However, in scene 3, the girls remain in character, but they recognise the presence of the audience and talk to them rather than each other. What is the effect of this? Why do you think that Mary Cutler has chosen to write the scene in this way?

The idea of characters talking to the audience is a very old one. In William Shakespeare's plays, characters often speak directly to the audience when they are either on their own or unobserved by other characters. We call this a *soliloquy*. The most famous of these is probably 'To be, or not to be . . .' from *Hamlet*. Find some examples of soliloquies and discuss what exactly the character is conveying to the audience. Some recent writers use this device widely. The German playwright Bertolt Brecht uses this device to make his audience realise that they are watching a play and not real life. Read the follow-up work to *The Smile*, to discover more about Brecht's theories on acting.

Character

The characters are paired off. Identify the pairings and decide which ones are likely to be successful.
Write brief thumbnail sketches of the characters.
For example:

JANE: Confident. Determined ('Keep your paws off Jim'). Gives impression of being experienced with boys. Demands attention. Tells Susie and Gem what to do.

Compare your notes. Discuss them. For instance, do you think Jane is really as experienced as she'd like to pretend?

Why do you think that Susie says that Gem is better off not knowing boys? Is this remark in contrast to other things she says?

Why do you think that Gem says that she wishes she was 'easy'? What does this reveal about her, and about Susie and Jane when they react with shock to this comment?

Hot seating

Use the hot seating technique described on page 165 in order to discover more about the characters. Hot seat them individually first then hot seat all three girls together and then all three boys. Finally, hot seat the various pairs. Are the answers that the characters give consistent or do they change depending upon who they are being hot seated with?

Improvisation

In her introduction Mary Cutler says that you begin writing a play when you can manage three people in a scene. Improvise a scene which involves three different people in a familiar situation, for example, a shop, a bus-stop. For some ideas on how to approach this improvisation read the follow-up work to Peter Terson's *How To Write a Play* in Volume 1 of *New Plays*.

Persuasion

Susie has to persuade her mother to allow her to have a party whilst her parents are out. Work in pairs. One person is a parent, the other is a daughter or son. The daughter or son has three minutes to persuade their parent to allow them to have a party. After three minutes reverse the roles. Discuss as a group the various ways of persuasion you used. Were some more effective than others? Have you ever used such arguments in real life?

Thoughts

In the follow-up exercises to *Little Old Lady* in Volume 1 of *New Plays*, you will find an exercise to help you explore what the characters are thinking as well as saying.

Try this for each of the characters. Take a scene, and for each of the characters select someone to act as their inner voice and speak their thoughts. Play the scene, with the characters giving their inner voices time to break in with their real thoughts. The inner voice need not do this every line; they may remain silent until they have something of interest to say. One *thought* in the whole scene could be sufficient if it reveals something unexpected about the character.

Extra scenes

This play provides an open invitation to explore as many extra scenes as you wish.

Play the party scene. Concentrate on Darren and Gem. Do they get on or not? How does the evening end?

Play a scene that takes place after the party, with the boys and girls separate once again.

Play a scene in which Susie's parents return unexpectedly.

Group discussion

How far do you think that the character's behaviour is influenced by what they imagine adults' behaviour to be like? How far is it influenced by what they think is expected of them?

In Britain, it is illegal to buy alcohol under the age of 18, yet many young people break this law. Conduct a survey in your group to discover how many people have broken this law. Do you think it is a good law? In some countries you have to be over 21 in order to purchase alcohol. Do you think that there should be an age limit? Should Britain's age limit be extended to stop people buying alcohol until they are 21?

Many people have had a party or asked their friends round when their parents are out for the evening or away for the weekend. Find out if any of your group have. Have there ever been any incidents at such parties which have involved parents finding out about such evenings?

Gem states that 'Boys are so difficult to talk to' and Jim says that Darren 'can only talk to girls if he's half sloshed'. Why do people get embarrassed when talking to the opposite sex?

Further reading

The Ghost in Volume 1 of *New Plays* also deals with a group of teenagers having a party whilst their parents are out. *The Pressure-Cooker*, in the same Volume, has a girl being two-timed by her boy-friend at a party.

For more work on Brecht and stylised acting see the further reading section to *The Smile* on page 146. For examples of Shakespeare's soliloquies see Act 1 Scene

1 of *Richard III*, the four main soliloquies in *Hamlet* and the several soliloquies that occur in *Macbeth*.

Fun City

by Barry Hines

In this play, as in *Breaking Point*, the distinction between hero and villain is not clear. Usually, a Headmaster would be a *goodie* and a thieving schoolboy, a *baddie*. However, Barry Hines undermines these supposed roles by creating a situation that makes us question the actions of Travis, even though Kyle is guilty of theft.

Exercises

Kyle lies about stealing the money. Try these two exercises to see how you fare when trying to deceive someone else.

Alibi

Two members of the group go outside the room. They are given some time to prepare an alibi (an excuse) as to where they were the previous evening. Meanwhile, the rest of the group prepares questions to ask the two suspects. One of the two re-enters the room. The group questions the person about the previous evening. When the group is satisfied that it has enough information from the suspect the second person is called in. The group asks similar questions, trying to crack the alibi. The group wins if the suspects' stories differ.

NB The pair must answer the questions and not claim that they cannot remember.

Deception

Divide the group into two teams. A member of team A makes a statement. Only that person knows if it is true. The opposing team must decide whether the statement is true or false. If the team is undecided then a majority vote is taken. A member of team B then makes a statement and so on. Points are awarded for a successful deception. The team with the most points at the end is the winner.

Interpretation

Plays are usually written for a reason. Writers often disguise their message in order to be more entertaining. It is up to us to find clues in the text to help us decide what the author's message is. We call this interpretation.

What would you describe as the main theme of the play and what issues are at stake?

The play takes place in the little world of the headmaster's study. However, the outside world occasionally intrudes. One social issue that is mentioned is the availability of video-nasties. Identify two other contemporary social issues that are mentioned in the play.

What is the significance of Travis' isometrics and exercises in helping our understanding of him?

Shearer states 'There are cheats at all games'. Who cheats in this play?

Character

The plot of the play is very simple: what makes *Fun City* interesting are the characters and the relationships between them. Travis and Kyle are poles apart; Shearer tries to bridge the gap between them but fails.

Read through the play again. For each character, write down four or five lines, spoken by him, that seem to you to sum up his character.

Besides the things they actually say, the actions of the characters give us an insight into their personalities. What hints as to character are given in the stage directions for Travis, Kyle and Shearer?

Hot seating

A further way of exploring character is to hot seat each character. This is a technique which allows us to question the characters and so find out more about them. The person playing the character we wish to question must answer *in role*, that is, in the role of the character.

Suppose we wish to hot seat Travis. The person playing the part of Travis might answer the questions of the class like this:

CLASS What made you think it was Kyle that stole the money?

TRAVIS Think? Think? I *knew* it was him. He's always in trouble. It was obviously him. Who else could it have been?

CLASS But you couldn't be sure, could you?

TRAVIS What on earth has that got to do with it? It *was* Kyle. I caught him out, didn't I? No pupil can get the better of me.

CLASS Did you think it was fair to tell the police, after Mr Shearer had promised Kyle not to tell them?

TRAVIS The boy is a thief! I don't care what Shearer said to him. He had no right to offer immunity.

Young teachers! I just don't know what the profession is coming to. Taking the side of a thief. If you ask me Shearer is as bad as Kyle. No discipline with these young teachers today. No discipline.

CLASS Why did you threaten to keep Kyle from his dinner?

TRAVIS I knew that would work! Get them through depriving them of something that matters to them. There's no point threatening them with detentions or lines. That's no deterrent. The cane! Now there's a deterrent. If I could have used that, I'd have had the truth out of him without all the bother.

CLASS Isn't that going too far?

TRAVIS Too far? What are you on about? Look I can't sit here answering stupid questions all day. I'm off now. Got to get some miles in. I'm running at the weekend. Healthy body, healthy mind, that's what I believe in. Maybe Kyle should get himself fit. Right, I'm off. Goodbye.

Use this technique to question other characters in the play. You could also hot seat characters that don't appear in the play, for example, other teachers, friends of Kyle or even his parents.

Extra scenes

We can also further our understanding of the characters by exploring incidents which do not happen in the play.

Here are some suggestions for further scenes you may wish to improvise or script:

A scene in which Kyle is interviewed by the police.
A scene in which Shearer describes the incident to a fellow teacher.

A scene in which Kyle's parents are informed about the theft.
A scene in which Kyle meets Shearer after he has been charged.

Role play

In a role play a member of the group takes on the character of another person. They must act as that person would, so, for instance, if the person is an old lady, then the member of the group must take on the characteristics of an old lady.

In a group role play, every member of the group takes the part of another person (takes on a role) then acts as that character would in an agreed situation.
This role play is of Kyle's trial. Appoint members of the group to take on the characters from the play. Also appoint magistrates, solicitors for the defence and prosecution. Other members of the group can be witnesses, for example, Social workers, Police, Teachers, Friends. Remember, it doesn't have to be correct in all legal details. What *is* important is to discover more about the characters and their situation.

Group discussion

Both Kyle and Travis deliberately lie. Kyle lies about stealing the money; Travis breaks his promise not to inform the police. Do you think Travis is right to call in the police?

Why do people tell lies?

Is there ever any justification for lying?

Kyle's appearance could not be called smart! Does this affect our view of Kyle before we know he is a thief? If it does, should it?

Shearer seems disgusted that Travis has held the threat of hunger over Kyle. Do you agree that this is an unfair tactic?
Should any form of threat be used in obtaining a confession to wrongdoing? If not, how can such confession be obtained and crime prevented?
Who do you feel most sympathy for at the end of the play?
Who do you feel is responsible for Kyle's predicament:
Kyle?
Shearer?
Travis?
The school system?
The owners of Fun City?
Kyle's parents and upbringing?
Society in general?
Discuss the influence each of the above may have had upon Kyle.

Further reading

Barry Hines is best known for his novel *Kes*, in which a young social outcast, Billy Casper, finds a purpose in life in training a young kestrel. There are many echoes of *Kes* in *Fun City*. You can read the story in play or novel form. There is also an excellent film, which is available on video. For a completely different examination of the issues of honesty and theft, read Terence Rattigan's *The Winslow Boy*. The historical and class differences between Rattigan's play and *Fun City* make an interesting comparison.

Freedom Log

by David Campton

Freedom Log was written for, and broadcast on, radio. Radio plays have become less popular since the invention of television, but still form a major part of the BBC's output. At their best they can appeal to the imagination in a way that television plays cannot. When Orson Welles broadcast his version of *War of the Worlds*, many Americans were convinced that Martians had actually landed on Earth! Some people even left their homes and fled to the hills in panic!

Comparisons

As in *Slave!* and *The Great Camel* in Volume 1 of *New Plays*, a narrator is used. The narrator is also one of the chief characters, Leyda, and the narration takes the form of a log. This is the same device that was used in the TV series *Star Trek*, where Captain Kirk's log was used to give the audience information about events which had happened. What do you think that David Campton achieves by using a narrator? Are there any other devices which he might have used instead?

How does the role of the narrator in *Freedom Log* differ from that in *The Smile*?

Many radio plays use a narrator as a link between the audience and the characters and events of the play. *Under Milk Wood* by Dylan Thomas is probably the greatest radio play ever written. Thomas uses not just one narrator but several during the course of the play. Anyone who is interested in radio drama should read *Under Milk Wood*, or hear a recording of it.

Project

Record *Freedom Log* on tape as a radio play. You will have to be very careful to get the sound effects right. Use an open reel tape if possible. This will allow you to edit the tape more easily than a cassette tape.
Recording sound effects can be a lot of fun, and you'll find unexpected things give the best results. There are also many excellent sound effects records and cassettes available. Think particularly about how to use sound effects to create the atmosphere of an alien planet. Try playing sounds backwards; to create alien birds, play normal birdsong backwards.
Also pay attention to the stage directions; how will you make it clear that Leyda is speaking the narration into the recording device?

Role play

This is based on *And Then There Were None*, a story by Eric Frank Russell. For an explanation of how to undertake a role play, look at the extension work to *Fun City* on page 167.

> A planet has been colonised by the followers of Mahatma Gandhi. They call themselves Gands and believe in non-violence and peaceful non-co-operation. All those who do not follow this way of life are called Anti-Gands. The Gands have no money but trade in favours and share all tasks equally. A favour is called an OB, short for obligation. Their motto is FIW meaning Freedom – I Won't! Another favourite expression is MYOB, short for Mind Your Own Business. This is said to people who ask questions the Gands do not wish to

answer. A spaceship of the Galactic Empire lands on the Gand's planet. Its mission is to crush any resistance offered and to capture the planet for the Empire. The heavily-armed soldiers seem to have an easy task: but how do you negotiate with leaders if there aren't any? And how do you crush resistance if none if offered?

This is the point at which the role play begins. Divide the group up into Gands and the crew of the Spaceship. The Gands have no leaders; the Empire does.

The crew of the spaceship must attempt to take over the planet: the Gands offer no resistance and may even try to convert the soldiers of the Empire to their way of thinking.

How is the situation resolved? Discuss the outcome and, if possible, read *And Then There Were None* to see what conclusions Eric Frank Russell came to. You can find it in *Science Fiction: The Great Years* edited by Carol and Frederick Pohl, published by Sphere.

Extra scenes

To help your understanding of the play, improvise further scenes in order to explore both character and situation. Here are some suggestions for you to work on:
A scene in which the mutiny takes place on board the spaceship.
A scene in which Boom and Snick disagree about sharing food.
Improvise Leyda's trial as a whole class role play.

Hot seating

Use the hot seating technique, described in the follow-up work to *Fun City* on page 165, to question Leyda, Boom and other mutineers.

Group discussion

We call democratic societies *free*, but we are only free in a democracy as long as we obey its laws. If we don't, and are caught, then our laws permit society to put us in prison. In a proper democracy, laws are decided by the will of the people, or by the majority. This is unfortunate if you are in the minority and you think that some laws are unfair.
What laws do you think are unfair and unjust?
Do we need laws?
Boom says he would like just a few laws, but Leyda says that once you have a few laws you have to keep making more. Is she right?
In small groups decide on a list of ten laws you would make. When all the groups have drafted these, as a whole class discuss the laws chosen. Compare the laws you have made with the Ten Commandments in The Bible.

Character

List the different reasons of Boom, Leyda and Snick for mutiny.
Why is Boom determined to have laws?
Why does Boom feel that he has to move against Leyda and her company?
David Campton clearly wants us to sympathise with Leyda's viewpoint. Does he achieve this aim? If he does, how does he manage to convince us of Leyda's argument? If he doesn't, why do we think that Boom is right?

Further reading

In the novel, *Lord of the Flies*, by William Golding, a group of children are marooned on an island. They have no contact with the outside world. Golding's description of what happens to their behaviour is horribly convincing.

The M & M Café

by Anne Aylor

Although *The M & M Café* is set in Mexico in 1957, it contains a set of characters who are immediately recognisable to a present-day audience. Anne Aylor uses the play to explore the idea of an outsider trying to become part of a close family relationship and how this attempt is perceived by both mother and daughter.

Character

The characters are of great importance in *The M & M Café*. Do the descriptions of the characters at the beginning of the play help your understanding of them?

Do they give you expectations of the characters and, if so, do they live up to them?

With which of the characters do you sympathise most? And least? Explain your reasons.

The characters are poor. Mona is a 'bottle blonde', Dolores a fast-food cook, Marshall is overweight and belches. In many books, films and plays such characters are treated without sympathy. In this play, however, all of the characters have great dignity.

One of the characters has to try very hard to be dignified. What is the result of this?

What does Marshall do to try and win Cato over? How do his efforts backfire?

What is Cato afraid of? Do you think her fear is justified?

Hot seating

Use the hot seating technique as described on page 165 in order to question all the characters. You could start with the following points:

Mona:	Does she love Marshall? Does she feel she has betrayed her husband's memory? Why is she 'ashamed' when she says: 'Cato everything happened so fast'?
Marshall:	Would he prefer Mona to be single rather than a widow? Was he lonely before he met Mona?
Dolores:	Is she a religious woman? Why does she hide until Cato has gone?

Cato is the most difficult character to question because she has the most problems and is therefore likely to give the most complicated answers. Hot seat Cato by using two different members of the group to question her. The two members should each take on a role. One of the two plays an impatient no-nonsense person who questions her along the lines of: 'Why are you being so stupid?' The other person should be more tolerant, understanding and sympathetic, perhaps her best friend. To the first person, Cato's replies would probably be defensive and angry, to the second, more honest and truthful.

Both persons should question Cato in turn. They may take suggestions from the rest of the group but no one else may address Cato directly.
Some points to explore: Does Cato really dislike Marshall? What does she feel about her mother? Why does she put on her mother's wedding dress? Why does she pray to St Francis?
Finally, hot seat all the characters. Ask them what they really want most in the world. Do you think they will all achieve what they want?

Interpretation

To say this play has a *moral*, suggests that its aim is to preach, which is not true. However, it does have a point to make. Can you identify what this point is?

Does a miracle really occur? If so, what is it and who actually performs the miracle? The Santo? or Dolores?

Do you think that this situation will be resolved happily, or are you pessimistic at the end of the play?

Extra scenes

Improvise a scene in which Cato learns that Mona is to marry Marshall.
Improvise a scene in which Cato's schoolfriends tease her about her mother's plans to remarry. Play the scene in two different ways: firstly, with Cato defending her mother's decisions and, secondly, with her joining in the attack on her mother. Which scene do you feel most comfortable with? Improvise an alternative ending to the story.

Group discussion

Marshall enjoys telling 'Aggie' jokes. An Aggie is a graduate or student at the Texas College of

Agriculture – in a wider sense, a farmer. In effect, Marshall is telling jokes at his own expense: why does he do this?
In the industrial cities of North America, people tend to tell jokes about Polish people. In England, the Irish are the butt of many jokes, and in France it is the Belgians. South Africans tell jokes about a half-witted Boer. His name is always Van der Meuwe, in the same way that the Irishmen in jokes are always called Paddy or Murphy.
Are these jokes harmless fun, or do they reinforce racial and cultural stereotypes? For example, Scotsmen are mean, Frenchmen are always romantic.
Why do we feel the need to label people like this?

Mona says to Cato 'You can't wait for perfection in this world. You take what happiness you can and run'. How far do you agree with this view? Do you feel it is an overstated, pessimistic view or a realistic one?
How far do you think single parents should listen to and respect their children's wishes when they decide to remarry? Does it make any difference whether their partners are dead (as Mona's) or separated and divorced?

Project

The theme of *The M & M Café* is a familiar one, to be found in comics, magazines and soap operas. Draw the events of the story as a comic strip. You can include earlier scenes, such as the funeral of Cato's father, or later ones, such as the wedding of Mona and Marshall. If you prefer you could use a camera and make up your own 'photostory' of the play.

Further reading

Compare the problems of these characters with those faced by the family in *Nuts*. Which situation do you think is the more hopeful? Another Peter Terson play, *The Weeping Madonna*, can be found in Volume 1 of *New Plays*. This also contains a saint, but is very different in tone and message to *The M & M Café*.

Breaking Point

by Steve Barlow

Breaking Point explores the issues of victimisation and prejudice. It is about a incident which has taken place before Wes and George meet.

Extra scenes

There are many scenes which you could script or improvise in order to help you explore the play further. Here are some suggestions:

The scene in which the loud-mouthed racist delivers his speech about sending blacks home. Pay particular attention to George's reaction, and what his mates say to him in order to calm him down.

A scene in which the police interview George about the incident. Does George admit he was there? Does he admit causing the injury? Or does he deny everything? Play the scene all three ways.

A scene in which Wes has to explain to another instructor, called Nick, that George has left the club and must not be allowed to join another. Nick is inclined to be insulting about black people. How can Wes make sure that Nick will refuse to train George without giving George away or agreeing with Nick's racist attitude?

Because of the nature of the attack, the police interview Wes as they suspect he may know the truth. Does Wes give George away or not? Play the interview.

A scene from George's life which may have made him feel bitter about racist attitudes.

Hot seating

Use the hot seating technique, as described on page 165, in order to discover more about the characters of Wes and George. Bear in mind some of the following points:

Hot seat Wes
When he first found out about the attack, why did he suspect George?
Why did he decide to tackle George himself and not report his suspicions to the police?
Why did he still not go to the police when he knew for certain that George was guilty?

Hot seat George
What did he think immediately after the attack?
Where did he go to after running away from the bus-stop?
Where had he been during the day before the meeting with Wes?

Hot seat Wes and George together
How do they feel towards each other now?
Has the meeting changed their views of each other?
The members of the group taking the parts of Wes and George must answer the questions in role, and may talk to each other in role during this hot seating session.

Interpretation

Who do you think Wes sympathises with: George, or the victim of his attack?

George explains that the racist remarks at the Lion were the last straw; he has been under unbearable tension for a long time as a result of everyday brushes with racist remarks. Do you think George's bitterness is justified?

People who look for, or expect to find, prejudice, invariably do find it, sometimes where it is not intended. Do you agree with this view? How many of George's problems might be of his own making?

George taunts Wes about getting old. This indicates that they get on together. What other evidence can you find that supports this view of their relationship?

The fact that it is snowing heavily explains why the two men are alone at the club, giving Wes the opportunity to test George. Does the snow have any other significance? Note that the last line of the play refers to the fact that it is still snowing.

Group discussion

Use the brainstorming technique described on page 144 in order to stimulate group discussion.

Prejudice

Racism is a form of prejudice which is generally based on skin-colour. However, it is also applied to people of a particular ethnic group who are, in appearance, no different from those who persecute them.

In a group brainstorm examples of racial prejudice, both general and particular. Is it possible to identify a common form racial prejudice takes?
Is it possible to discover a starting-point for racial prejudice?

Brainstorm examples of other varieties of prejudice. How similar or different are they to racial prejudice? Are prejudices ever based on a combination of factors? For example, if someone was prejudiced against Arabs would it be on racial, religious, political or economic grounds or a combination of these?

How is prejudice shown? Brainstorm the various ways in which people may demonstrate their prejudice.

Words

Is it possible that racist attitudes are influenced by the interpretation we place on the words *black* and *white* in different contexts?
The phrase 'play the white man' means that the person addressed is expected to behave generously: while 'he's not as black as he's painted' means a person has an undeserved poor reputation. Both of these phrases, by implication, show the idea of white representing virtue and black vice.

Brainstorm as many examples of this type of use of the words *black* and *white* as possible. Discuss their uses.

Role play

Prejudice is sometimes based not on what a person *is* but on what they *do*. A person who works during a strike may become an instant outcast, socially unacceptable to other members of the workforce.

This group role play explores such an incident. (For information on the technique of role play, see page 167.)
This role play is set in a social club. Set up the room to imitate the layout of such a club (tables, chairs, pool table, dartboard, fruit machine, bar, etc.) All the group members are workers at the same factory (some maybe the wives, husbands, boy-friends or girl-friends of workers).
One person is sent out of the room. They are told that a piece of information is to be given concerning them, for example, they have just won the pools. This information will affect the way people react to them.
When the person has gone out the following information is given. The workers have been on strike. The person outside was a strike breaker. This person is to be totally ignored. No one may speak to them or even acknowledge their existence.
The person outside then re-enters and the role play begins.
After an allotted time, stop the role play and discuss the experience.

Exercise

Invent a prejudice

A member of the group decides on a prejudice. It must not be a *rational* or well-known one, but should be something totally ridiculous. For example, the person may be prejudiced against people with blue eyes or those wearing a red article of clothing. The group members then walk round the room talking to others. The person who has invented the prejudice also walks around, gathering together those people who are not included in the prejudice. This continues until all the

subjects of the prejudice are isolated from the remainder. Care must be taken not to reveal the nature of the prejudice.
The victims of discrimination must then try and guess the nature of the prejudice. Discuss the experience and then choose another person to invent a different prejudice.

Further reading

There are many plays, novels and poems which deal with the issue of prejudice in its various forms. Harper Lee's classic novel *To Kill a Mockingbird*, deals with racism in the Southern States of the USA. The creator of Alf Garnet, Johnny Speight, looks at the theme of prejudice in his play *If There Weren't Any Blacks You'd Have to Invent Them*. David Edgar also explores the issues of racism in *Destiny*, a play about a National Front politician.